아서와
혼비백산 클럽

CONTENTS

대한민국 영어 학습자라면 꼭 한번 읽어봐야 할, 아서 챕터북 시리즈!

아서 챕터북 시리즈(Arthur Chapter Book series)는 미국의 작가 마크 브라운(Marc Brown)이 쓴 책입니다. 레이크우드 초등학교에 다니는 주인공 아서(Arthur)가 소소한 일상에서 벌이는 다양한 에피소드를 담은 이 책은, 기본적으로 미국 초등학생들을 위해 쓰인 책이지만 누구나 공감할 만한 재미있는 스토리로 출간된 지 30년이 넘은 지금까지 남녀노소 모두에게 큰 사랑을 받고 있습니다. 아서가 주인공으로 등장하는 이야기는 리더스북과 챕터북 등 다양한 형태로 출판되었는데, 현재 미국에서만 누적 판매 부수가 6천6백만 부를 돌파한 상황으로 대한민국 인구 숫자보다 더 많은 책이 판매된 것을 생각하면 그 인기가 어느 정도 인지 실감할 수 있습니다.

특히 이『아서 챕터북』은 한국에서 영어 학습자를 위한 최적의 원서로 큰 사랑을 받고 있기도 합니다.『영어 낭독 훈련』,『잠수네 영어 학습법』,『솔빛이네 엄마표 영어연수』등 많은 영어 학습법 책들에서『아서 챕터북』을 추천 도서로 선정하고 있으며, 수많은 영어 고수들과 영어 선생님들, '엄마표 영어'를 진행하는 부모님들에게도 반드시 거쳐 가야 하는 영어원서로 전폭적인 지지를 얻고 있습니다.

번역과 단어장이 포함된 워크북, 그리고 오디오북까지 담긴 풀 패키지!

이 책은 이렇게 큰 사랑을 받고 있는 영어원서『아서 챕터북』시리즈에, 더욱 탁월한 학습 효과를 거둘 수 있도록 다양한 콘텐츠를 덧붙인 책입니다.

• 영어원서: 본문에 나온 어려운 어휘에 볼드 처리가 되어 있어 단어를 더욱 분명히 인지하며 자연스럽게 암기하게 됩니다.
• 단어장: 원서에 나온 어려운 어휘가 '한영'은 물론 '영영' 의미까지 완벽하게 정리되어 있으며, 반복되는 단어까지 넣어두어 자연스럽게 복습이 되도록 구성했습니다.
• 번역: 영어와 비교할 수 있도록 직역에 가까운 번역을 담았습니다. 원서 읽기에 익숙하지 않는 초보 학습자들도 어려움 없이 내용을 파악할 수 있습니다.
• 퀴즈: 현직 원어민 교사가 만든 이해력 점검 퀴즈가 들어있습니다.
• 오디오북: 미국 현지에서 판매중인 빠른 속도의 오디오북(분당 약 145단어)과

국내에서 녹음된 따라 읽기용 오디오북(분당 약 110단어)을 포함하고 있어 듣기 훈련은 물론 소리 내어 읽기에까지 폭넓게 사용할 수 있습니다.

이 책의 수준과 타깃 독자
- 미국 원어민 기준: 유치원 ~ 초등학교 저학년
- 한국 학습자 기준: 초등학교 저학년 ~ 중학교 1학년
- 영어원서 완독 경험이 없는 초보 영어 학습자 (토익 기준 450~750점대)
- 비슷한 수준의 다른 챕터북: Magic Tree House, Marvin Redpost, The Zack Files, Captain Underpants
- 도서 분량: 5,000단어 초반 (약 5,000~5,200단어)

아서 챕터북, 이렇게 읽어보세요!

- **단어 암기는 이렇게!** 처음 리딩을 시작하기 전, 해당 챕터에 나오는 단어들을 눈으로 쭉 훑어봅니다. 모르는 단어는 좀 더 주의 깊게 보되, 손으로 써가면서 완벽하게 암기할 필요는 없습니다. 본문을 읽으면서 이 단어들을 다시 만나게 되는데, 그 과정에서 단어의 쓰임새와 어감을 자연스럽게 익히게 됩니다. 이렇게 책을 읽은 후에, 단어를 다시 한번 복습하세요. 복습할 때는 중요하다고 생각하는 단어들을 손으로 써가면서 꼼꼼하게 외우는 것도 좋습니다. 이런 방식으로 책을 읽다보면, 많은 단어를 빠르고 부담 없이 익히게 됩니다.

- **리딩할 때는 리딩에만 집중하자!** 원서를 읽는 중간 중간 모르는 단어가 나온다고 워크북을 들춰보거나, 곧바로 번역을 찾아보는 것은 매우 좋지 않은 습관입니다. 모르는 단어나 이해가 가지 않는 문장이 나온다고 해도 펜으로 가볍게 표시만 해두고, 전체적인 맥락을 잡아가며 빠르게 읽어나가세요. 리딩을 할 때는 속도에 대한 긴장감을 잃지 않으면서 리딩에만 집중하는 것이 좋습니다. 모르는 단어와 문장은, 리딩이 끝난 후에 한꺼번에 정리해보는 '리뷰'시간을 갖습니다. 리뷰를 할 때는 번역은 물론 단어장과 사전도 꼼꼼하게 확인하면서 왜 이해가 되지 않았는지 확인해 봅니다.

- **번역 활용은 이렇게!** 이해가 가지 않는 문장은 번역을 통해서 그 의미를 파악할

수 있습니다. 하지만 한국어와 영어는 정확히 1:1 대응이 되지 않기 때문에 번역을 활용하는 데에도 지혜가 필요합니다. 의역이 된 부분까지 억지로 의미를 대응해서 암기하려고 하기보다, 어떻게 그런 의미가 만들어진 것인지 추측하면서 번역은 참고자료로 활용하는 것이 좋습니다.

- **듣기 훈련은 이렇게!** 리스닝 실력을 향상시키길 원한다면 오디오북을 적극적으로 활용하세요. 처음에는 오디오북을 틀어놓고 눈으로 해당 내용을 따라 읽으면서 훈련을 하고, 이것이 익숙해지면 오디오북만 틀어놓고 '귀를 통해' 책을 읽어보세요. 눈으로는 한 번도 읽지 않은 책을 귀를 통해 완벽하게 이해할 수 있다면 이후에는 영어 듣기로 고생하는 일은 거의 없을 것입니다.

- **소리 내어 읽고 녹음하자!** 이 책은 특히 소리 내어 읽기(Voice Reading)에 최적화된 문장 길이와 구조를 가지고 있습니다. 또한 오디오북 CD에 포함된 '따라 읽기용' 오디오북으로 소리 내어 읽기 훈련을 함께할 수 있습니다. 소리 내어 읽기를 하면서 내가 읽은 것을 녹음하고 들어보세요! 자신의 영어 발음을 들어보는 것은 몹시 민망한 일이지만, 그 과정을 통해서 의식적·무의식적으로 발음을 교정하게 됩니다. 이렇게 영어로 소리를 만들어 본 경험은 이후 탄탄한 스피킹 실력의 밑거름이 될 것입니다.

- **2~3번 반복해서 읽자!** 영어 초보자라면 2~3회 반복해서 읽을 것을 추천합니다. 초보자일수록 처음 읽을 때는 생소한 단어들과 스토리 때문에 내용 파악에 급급할 수밖에 없습니다. 하지만 일단 내용을 파악한 후에 다시 읽으면 어휘와 문장 구조 등 다른 부분까지 관찰하면서 조금 더 깊이 있게 읽을 수 있고, 그 과정에서 리딩 속도도 빨라지고 리딩 실력을 더 확고하게 다지게 됩니다.

- **'시리즈'로 꾸준히 읽자!** 한 작가의 책을 시리즈로 읽는 것 또한 영어 실력 향상에 큰 도움이 됩니다. 같은 등장인물이 다시 나오기 때문에 내용 파악이 더 수월할 뿐 아니라, 작가가 사용하는 어휘와 표현들도 자연스럽게 반복되기 때문에 탁월한 복습 효과까지 얻을 수 있습니다. 『아서 챕터북』 시리즈는 현재 10권, 총 50,000단어 분량이 출간되어 있습니다. 이 책들을 시리즈로 꾸준히 읽으면서 영어 실력을 쑥쑥 향상시켜 보세요!

영어원서 본문 구성

내용이 담긴 본문입니다.

원어민이 읽는 일반 원서와 같은 텍스트지만, 암기해야 할 중요 어휘들은 볼드체로 표시되어 있습니다. 이 어휘들은 지금 들고 계신 워크북에 챕터별로 정리되어 있습니다.

학습 심리학 연구 결과에 따르면, 한 단어씩 따로 외우는 단어 암기는 거의 효과가 없다고 합니다. 대신 단어를 제대로 외우기 위해서는 문맥(Context) 속에서 단어를 암기해야 하며, 한 단어 당 문맥 속에서 15번 이상 마주칠 때 완벽하게 암기할 수 있다고 합니다.

이 책의 본문은 중요 어휘를 볼드로 강조하여, 문맥 속의 단어들을 더 확실히 인지(Word Cognition in Context)하도록 돕고 있습니다. 또한 대부분의 중요한 단어들은 다른 챕터에서도 반복해서 등장하기 때문에 이 책을 읽는 것만으로도 자연스럽게 어휘력을 향상시킬 수 있습니다.

또한 본문에는 내용 이해를 돕기 위해 '각주'가 첨가되어 있습니다. 각주는 굳이 암기할 필요는 없지만, 알아두면 내용을 더 깊이 있게 이해할 수 있어 원서를 읽는 재미가 배가됩니다.

워크북(Workbook)의 구성

Check Your Reading Speed

해당 챕터의 단어 수가 기록되어 있어, 리딩 속도를 측정할 수 있습니다. 특히 리딩 속도를 중시하는 독자들이 유용하게 사용할 수 있습니다.

Build Your Vocabulary

본문에 볼드 표시되어 있는 단어들이 정리되어 있습니다. 리딩 전, 후에 반복해서 보면 원서를 더욱 쉽게 읽을 수 있고, 어휘력도 빠르게 향상됩니다.

단어는 〈빈도 – 스펠링 – 발음기호 – 품사 – 한글 뜻 – 영문 뜻〉 순서로 표기되어 있으며 빈도 표시(★)가 많을수록 필수 어휘입니다. 반복 등장하는 단어는 빈도 대신 '복습'으로 표기되어 있습니다. 품사는 아래와 같이 표기했습니다.

n. 명사 | a. 형용사 | ad. 부사 | v. 동사
conj. 접속사 | prep. 전치사 | int. 감탄사 | idiom 숙어 및 관용구

Comprehension Quiz

간단한 퀴즈를 통해 읽은 내용에 대한 이해력을 점검해 볼 수 있습니다.

번역

영문과 비교할 수 있도록 최대한 직역에 가까운 번역을 담았습니다.

오디오북 CD 구성

이 책은 '듣기 훈련'과 '소리 내어 읽기 훈련'을 위한 2가지 종류의 오디오북이 포함되어 있습니다.

- 듣기 훈련용 오디오북: 분당 145단어 속도 (미국 현지 판매 중인 오디오북)
- 소리 내어 읽기 훈련용 오디오북: 분당 110 단어 속도

오디오북은 MP3 파일로 제공되는 MP3 기기나 컴퓨터에 옮겨서 사용하셔야 합니다. 오디오북에 이상이 있을 경우 helper@longtailbooks.co.kr로 메일을 주시면 자세한 안내를 받으실 수 있습니다.

EBS 동영상 강의 안내

EBS의 어학사이트(EBSlang.co.kr)에서 『아서 챕터북』 동영상 강의가 진행되고 있습니다.
영어 어순의 원리에 맞게 빠르고 정확하게 이해하는 법을 완벽하게 코치해주는 국내 유일의 강의!
저렴한 수강료에 완강 시 50% 환급까지!
지금 바로 열광적인 수강 평가와 샘플 강의를 확인하세요!

http://Arthur.EnglishWish.com

Chapter 1

1. What was worse than being patient for D.W.?

A. Being shown to be patient

B. Being told to be patient

C. Having to wait for other people

D. Seeing other people hurry

2. What was Mr. Read making in the kitchen?

A. He was making pancakes.

B. He was making bagels.

C. He was making waffles.

D. He was making French toast.

3. What happened when Arthur bumped into his father?

A. Arthur was covered in powdered sugar.

B. Mr. Read dropped all of the waffles on the floor.

C. Arthur had to eat cold cereal instead.

D. Mr. Read caught all of the waffles on the platter.

4. Why was Arthur in such a hurry to the library?

A. He wanted to study with his friends and finish his homework.

B. He wanted to meet his friends there and go play in the park.

C. He wanted to read a new book that was coming to the library.

D. He wanted to go play computer games with his friends.

5. Why did D.W. think that it was great that Arthur was going to the library?

A. D.W. got to eat more waffles.

B. D.W. wanted Arthur to do well in school.

C. D.W. could play in Arthur's room when he was gone.

D. D.W. wanted Arthur to bring her back a book.

Check Your Reading Speed

1분에 몇 단어를 읽는지 리딩 속도를 측정해보세요.

$$\frac{498 \text{ words}}{\text{reading time ( ) sec}} \times 60 = (\quad) \text{ WPM}$$

Build Your Vocabulary

breakfast [brékfəst] n. 아침식사
Breakfast is the first meal of the day. It is usually eaten in the early part of the morning.

patient [péiʃənt] a. 인내심[참을성] 있는; n. 환자
If you are patient, you stay calm and do not get annoyed, for example when something takes a long time, or when someone is not doing what you want them to do.

drum [drʌm] v. (손가락으로) 탁탁 치다, (발로) 쿵쿵 구르다; 북을 치다; n. 북, 드럼
If something drums on a surface, or if you drum something on a surface, it hits it regularly, making a continuous beating sound.

stove [stouv] n. (요리용 가스·전기) 레인지; 스토브, 난로
A stove is a piece of equipment which provides heat, either for cooking or for heating a room.

brown [braun] v. 노릇노릇하게 타게 하다, 살짝 굽다; a. 갈색의; n. 갈색
When food browns or when you brown food, you cook it, usually for a short time on a high flame.

powder [páudər] v. ~을 가루로 만들다; n. 가루, 분말 (powdered a. 분말이 된)
A powdered substance is one which is in the form of a powder although it can come in a different form.

yum [jʌm] int. 냠냠(맛있는 것을 생각하며 내는 소리)
People sometimes say 'yum' or 'yum yum' to show that they think
something tastes or smells very good.

lick [lik] v. 핥다; n. 한 번 핥기, 핥아먹기
When people or animals lick something, they move their tongue across
its surface.

high chair [hai ʧɛər] n. (식사 때의 어린이용) 높은 의자, 유아용 의자
A high chair is a chair with long legs for a small child to sit in while they
are eating.

rev [rev] v. (내연 기관 등의) 회전 속도를 올리다 (rev up idiom 활기를 띠다, 흥분하다)
If someone is revved up, they are prepared for an important or exciting
activity.

platter [plǽtər] n. (타원형의 얕은) 큰 접시
A platter is a large, flat plate used for serving food.

announce [ənáuns] v. 알리다, 공고하다, 전하다
If you announce a piece of news or an intention, especially something
that people may not like, you say it loudly and clearly, so that everyone
you are with can hear it.

request [rikwést] n. 부탁, 요구; v. 신청하다, 바라다
If you make a request, you politely or formally ask someone to do
something.

president [prézədənt] n. 대통령; 장(長), 회장
The president of a country that has no king or queen is the person who
is the head of state of that country.

professional [prəféʃənl] a. 전문의, 프로의; 직업의; n. 프로 선수, 직업인
You use professional to describe people who do a particular thing to
earn money rather than as a hobby.

athlete [ǽθliːt] n. 운동선수, 스포츠맨
An athlete is a person who does a sport, especially athletics, or track
and field events.

‡ **grain** [grein] n. 곡물, 곡류; 낟알 (whole-grain n. 통밀, 정제하지 않은 곡물)
Grain is a cereal crop, especially wheat or corn, that has been harvested and is used for food or in trade.

* **goodness** [gúdnis] n. (음식의) 자양분; 우수성, 좋은 상태; 선량, 친절
Goodness is the quality of being kind, helpful, and honest.

‡ **bite** [bait] n. 한 입(의 분량); 물기, 물어뜯기; v. 물다, 물어뜯다
A bite is the amount of food you take into your mouth when you bite it.

‡ **serve** [sə:rv] v. (음식을) 제공하다; 일하다, 복무하다
When you serve food and drink, you give people food and drink.

‡ **rush** [rʌʃ] v. 돌진하다; 급히 움직이다, 서두르다; n. 돌진; 분주, 바쁨
If you rush somewhere, you go there quickly.

‡ **unexpected** [ʌnikspéktid] a. 예기치 않은, 예상 밖의 (unexpectedly ad. 뜻밖에)
If an event or someone's behavior is unexpected, it surprises you because you did not think that it was likely to happen.

* **collide** [kəláid] v. 충돌하다, 부딪치다; (의지·목적 등이) 일치하지 않다, 상충하다
If two or more moving people or objects collide, they crash into one another.

‡ **knock** [nak] v. 부딪치다, 충돌하다; (문을) 두드리다, 노크하다
If you knock something, you touch or hit it roughly, especially so that it falls or moves.

* **gasp** [gæsp] v. 숨이 턱 막히다, 헉 하고 숨을 쉬다; n. (숨이 막히는 듯) 헉 하는 소리를 냄
When you gasp, you take a short quick breath through your mouth, especially when you are surprised, shocked, or in pain.

spring into action idiom 갑자기 행동[작동]하기 시작하다
If someone springs into action or to life, they suddenly become active or start to work.

‡ **dish** [diʃ] v. 접시에 담다[담아서 내다]; n. 접시; 요리, 음식
If you dish food up, you serve it by putting it on plates.

clap [klæp] v. 박수를 치다; n. 박수 (소리)
When you clap, you hit your hands together to show appreciation or attract attention.

bow [bau] n. (고개 숙여 하는) 인사, 절; v. 머리를 숙이다, 절하다
When you take a bow to someone, you briefly bend your body toward them as a formal way of greeting them or showing respect.

spend [spend] v. (시간을) 보내다, 지내다; (돈·자원을) 쓰다, 소비하다
If you spend time or energy doing something, you use your time or effort doing it.

wait on idiom 식사 시중을 들다, (손님에게) 응대하다
If you wait on someone, you bring food and drink to them at a table, usually in a restaurant.

push one's luck idiom 운을 너무 믿고 덤비다
If you say that someone is pushing their luck, you think they are taking a bigger risk than is sensible, and may get into trouble.

agree [əgríː] v. 동의하다, 찬성하다
If you agree with an action or suggestion, you approve of it.

stuff [stʌf] v. 채워 넣다, 채우다; n. 것(들), 물건, 물질
If you stuff something somewhere, you push it there quickly and roughly.

choke [ʧouk] v. 질식시키다, 숨이 막히다; n. 질식
When you choke or when something chokes you, you cannot breathe properly or get enough air into your lungs.

impress [imprés] v. 깊은 인상을 주다, 감명을 주다 (impressed a. 감명을 받은)
If something impresses you, you feel great admiration for it.

free will [friː wíl] n. (인간의) 자유 의지, 자의
If you do something of your own free will, you do it by choice and not because you are forced to do it.

argue [ɑ́ːrgjuː] v. 논쟁하다, 주장하다
If one person argues with another, they speak angrily to each other about something that they disagree about.

exaggerate [igzǽdʒərèit] v. 과장하다
If you exaggerate, you indicate that something is, for example, worse or more important than it really is.

shelf [ʃelf] n. (pl. shelves) 책꽂이, (책장의) 칸; 선반
A shelf is a flat piece which is attached to a wall or to the sides of a cupboard for keeping books.

just about idiom 거의 (다)
You use just about to indicate that what you are talking about is so close to being the case that it can be regarded as being the case.

popular [pápjulər] a. 인기 있는; 대중적인; 일반적인
Something that is popular is enjoyed or liked by a lot of people.

sort of [sɔ́ːrt əv] ad. 얼마간, 다소; 일종의
You use sort of when you want to say that your description of something is not very accurate.

scary [skέəri] a. 무서운, 두려운
Something that is scary is rather frightening.

unusual [ʌnjúːʒuəl] a. 독특한, 유별난
If something is unusual, it does not happen very often or you do not see it or hear it very often.

combination [kàmbənéiʃən] n. 결합, 화합, 조합
A combination of things is a mixture of them.

swallow [swálou] v. 삼키다, 목구멍으로 넘기다; (초조해서) 마른침을 삼키다
If you swallow something, you cause it to go from your mouth down into your stomach.

dash [dæʃ] v. 돌진하다, 서둘러 가다; 내던지다; n. 돌진, 질주
If you dash somewhere, you run or go there quickly and suddenly.

big deal [bíg díːl] n. 대단한 것, 큰 일
If you say that something is a big deal, you mean that it is important or significant in some way.

eye [ai] v. (탐이 나거나 의심스러워) 쳐다보다; n. (한쪽) 눈
If you eye someone or something in a particular way, you look at them carefully in that way.

Chapter

2

1. **What was Arthur thinking about on his way to the library?**

   A. He was thinking about writing his own scary story.

   B. He was thinking about the waffles he father had made for breakfast.

   C. He was thinking about the new book he would be reading soon.

   D. He was thinking about how many other children would be at the library.

2. **Why did Arthur jump over the storm grate on his way to the library?**

   A. There was a puddle and he did not want to get wet.

   B. He had dropped a book down one before.

   C. He was exercising on his way to the library.

   D. He did not want a creature from one of the books to get him.

3. **What troubled Arthur when he arrived at the library?**

   A. The library was closed for the day.

   B. There was a long line of kids already there.

   C. He could not find his friends in the line.

   D. The author of the new book was signing copies.

4. **Who else was at the library besides children?**

   A. TV reporters

   B. Teachers

   C. Writers

   D. Parents

5. **What message did the library have for the children?**

   A. The author of the Scare-Your-Pants-Off Club books was sick.

   B. The newest Scare-Your-Pants-Off Club book was delayed by one day.

   C. There was only one copy of the newest Scare-Your-Pants-Off Club book.

   D. All of the Scare-Your-Pants-Off Club books including the new one had been removed.

1분에 몇 단어를 읽는지 리딩 속도를 측정해보세요.

$$\frac{546 \text{ words}}{\text{reading time ( ) sec}} \times 60 = (\quad) \text{ WPM}$$

Build Your Vocabulary

wonder [wʌ́ndər] v. 호기심을 가지다, 이상하게 여기다; n. 경탄할 만한 것, 경이
If you wonder about something, you think about it because it interests you and you want to know more about it.

witch [witʃ] n. 마녀
In fairy stories, a witch is a woman, usually an old woman, who has evil magic powers.

shiver [ʃívər] v. (추위·두려움·흥분 등으로) (몸을) 떨다; n. 전율, 몸서리
When you shiver, your body shakes slightly because you are cold or frightened.

grate [greit] n. 배수구 뚜껑; (난로 안의 연료를 받치는) 쇠살대
(storm grate n. 빗물 배수구)
A storm grate is a drainage hole that carries water or sewage away from a place, or an opening in a surface that leads to the pipe.

creature [kríːtʃər] n. 생물, 창조물
You can refer to any living thing that is not a plant as a creature, especially when it is of an unknown or unfamiliar kind.

grab [græb] v. 부여잡다, 움켜쥐다; n. 부여잡기
If you grab something, you take it or pick it up suddenly and roughly.

sort of [sɔ́ːrt əv] ad. 일종의; 얼마간, 다소
If you talk about a particular sort of something, you are talking about a class of things that have particular features in common.

careless [kέərlis] a. 쓸데없는, 부주의한; 무관심한 (carelessness n. 경솔, 부주의)
If you are careless, you do not pay enough attention to what you are doing, and so you make mistakes, or cause harm or damage.

cost [kɔːst] v. 희생시키다; 비용이 들다, (사람에게 ~을) 잃게 하다; n. 희생; 값, 비용
If an event or mistake costs you something, you lose that thing as the result of it.

dearly [díərli] ad. 큰 대가를 치르고, 값비싸게; 대단히, 몹시
If you pay dearly for doing something or if it costs you dearly, you suffer a lot as a result.

form [fɔːrm] v. 형성되다, 구성하다, 만들어 내다; n. 모양, 형태
When a particular shape forms or is formed, people or things move or are arranged so that this shape is made.

snake [sneik] v. (길 등이) 꾸불꾸불 이어지다, 꿈틀거리다; n. 뱀
Something that snakes in a particular direction goes in that direction in a line with a lot of bends.

sidewalk [sáidwɔ́ːk] n. (포장한) 보도, 인도
A sidewalk is a path with a hard surface by the side of a road.

wave [weiv] v. 흔들다, 신호하다; 파도치다; n. 파도, 물결
If you wave or wave your hand, you move your hand from side to side in the air, usually in order to say hello or goodbye to someone.

trudge [trʌdʒ] v. 터벅터벅 걷다; n. 터덕터덕 걸음
If you trudge somewhere, you walk there slowly and with heavy steps, especially because you are tired or unhappy.

unbelievable [ʌ̀nbilíːvəbl] a. 믿을 수 없는, 놀랄 만한
You can use unbelievable to emphasize that you think something is very bad or shocking.

dawn [dɔːn] n. 새벽, 동틀 녘; v. 날이 새다, 밝아지다
Dawn is the time of day when light first appears in the sky, just before the sun rises.

jump to conclusions idiom 성급한 결론[판단]을 내리다, 속단하다
If you say that someone jumps to conclusions, you are critical of them because they decide too quickly that something is true, when they do not know all the facts.

* **conclude** [kənklúːd] v. 결론짓다, 끝내다 (conclusion n. 결론, 결말)
If you conclude that something is true, you decide that it is true using the facts you know as a basis.

* **yawn** [jɔːn] v. 하품하다; n. 하품
If you yawn, you open your mouth very wide and breathe in more air than usual, often when you are tired or when you are not interested in something.

* **sigh** [sai] v. 한숨 쉬다; n. 한숨, 탄식
When you sigh, you let out a deep breath, as a way of expressing feelings such as disappointment, tiredness, or pleasure.

check out idiom (도서관 등에서) 대출받다
If you check out, you borrow something such as a book or a video from a library.

* **nod** [nad] v. (고개를) 끄덕이다, 끄덕여 나타내다; n. (고개를) 끄덕임
If you nod, you move your head downward and upward to show agreement, understanding, or approval.

* **curse** [kəːrs] n. 저주, 악담; v. 저주하다, 욕설을 퍼붓다
You can refer to something that causes a great deal of trouble or harm as a curse.

* **mummy** [mʌ́mi] n. 미라
A mummy is a dead body which was preserved long ago by being rubbed with special oils and wrapped in cloth.

* **breath** [breθ] n. 숨, 호흡; 한 번 들이마시기, 한 번 쉬기
Your breath is the air that you let out through your mouth when you breathe.

* **brush** [brʌʃ] v. (솔이나 손으로) 털다; 솔질하다
(brush one's teeth idiom 이를 닦다, 양치질을 하다)
If you brush your teeth, you clean your teeth with toothbrush and toothpaste.

* **skeleton** [skélətn] n. 해골; 골격, 뼈대
Your skeleton is the framework of bones in your body.

* **closet** [klázit] n. 벽장
A closet is a piece of furniture with doors at the front and shelves inside, which is used for storing things.

* **roll** [roul] v. 구르다, 굴러가다[오다]; 굴리다; n. 굴리기, 던지기; 통, 두루마리
When something rolls or when you roll it, it moves along a surface, turning over many times.

* **substitute** [sʌ́bstitjùːt] n. (다른 누구·무엇을) 대신하는 사람[것];
v. 대신하다, 교체되다 (substitute teacher n. 대체[대리] 교사)
A substitute teacher is a teacher whose job is to take the place of other teachers at different schools when they are unable to be there.

* **shudder** [ʃʌ́dəːr] v. 떨다, 몸서리치다; n. 떨림, 전율
If you shudder, you shake with fear, horror, or disgust, or because you are cold.

never mind idiom 쓸데없는 소리하지 마라; 걱정하지 마라
You use never mind to tell someone that they need not do something or worry about something, because it is not important or because you will do it yourself.

creak [kriːk] v. 삐걱거리다, 삐걱거리게 하다; n. 삐걱거리는 소리
If something creaks, it makes a short, high-pitched sound when it moves.

sinister [sínəstər] a. 불길한; 사악한, 음흉한
Something that is sinister seems evil or harmful.

* **shadow** [ʃǽdou] n. 그림자; 그늘, 어둠
A shadow is a dark shape on a surface that is made when something stands between a light and the surface.

librarian [laibrέəriən] n. (도서관의) 사서
A librarian is a person who is in charge of a library or who has been specially trained to work in a library.

turnout [tɔ́:rnàut] n. (구경·행렬 등에) 나온 사람들, (집회 등의) 출석자(수), 집합
The turnout at an event is the number of people who go to it or take part in it.

cheer [ʧiər] v. 환호성을 지르다, 응원하다; n. 환호(성)
When people cheer, they shout loudly to show their approval or to encourage someone who is doing something such as taking part in a game.

crowd [kraud] n. 군중, 인파; 많은 것, 다수; v. 모여들다, 붐비다
A crowd is a large group of people who have gathered together, for example to watch or listen to something interesting, or to protest about something.

remove [rimú:v] v. 치우다, 제거하다; 이동하다, 떠나다
If you remove something from a place, you take it away.

shelf [ʃelf] n. (pl. shelves) 책꽂이, (책장의) 칸; 선반
A shelf is a flat piece which is attached to a wall or to the sides of a cupboard for keeping books.

further [fɔ́:rðər] a. 더 이상의, 추가의; ad. 더욱 더, 더 멀리에
You use further to introduce a statement that relates to the same general topic and that gives additional information or makes an additional point.

notice [nóutis] n. 통지, 통보; 주의, 주목; v. 알아차리다, 주의하다
If you give notice about something that is going to happen, you give a warning in advance that it is going to happen.

stun [stʌn] v. 어리벙벙하게 하다; 기절시키다; n. 놀라게 함 (**stunned** a. 어리벙벙한)
If you are stunned by something, you are extremely shocked or surprised by it and are therefore unable to speak or do anything.

let out idiom (울음소리·신음소리 등을) 내다
If you let out a cry or a sigh, you make a sound.

* **shriek** [ʃriːk] n. 비명; v. 새된 소리를 지르다, 비명을 지르다
A shriek is a short, very loud cry.

disbelief [dìsbilíːf] n. 믿기지 않음, 불신감
Disbelief is not believing that something is true or real.

* **fair** [fɛər] ① a. 타당한, 온당한; 공정한, 공평한 ② n. 축제 마당; 박람회, 품평회
Something or someone that is fair is reasonable, right, and just.

* **naturally** [nǽtʃərəli] ad. 물론, 당연히; 자연 발생적으로, 저절로
You use naturally to indicate that you think something is very obvious and not at all surprising in the circumstances.

* **rush** [rʌʃ] v. 급히 움직이다, 서두르다; 돌진하다; n. 분주, 바쁨; 돌진
If people rush to do something, they do it as soon as they can, because they are very eager to do it.

Chapter 3

1. **What did Arthur and his friends see on the news?**

   A. They saw a report on the event at the library.

   B. They saw a report on the lives of librarians.

   C. They saw a report on a famous author at the library.

   D. They saw a report on children not studying hard enough.

2. **Why had the Scare-Your-Pants-Off Club books been removed from the library?**

   A. A parents group said that kids needed to focus on studying.

   B. A parents group said the scary stories were boring to kids.

   C. A parents group said the library should focus on literature.

   D. A parents group said the scary stories were bad for kids.

3. **How did Arthur's friends react to him saying they never gave up before?**

   A. They said there was a first time for everything.

   B. They said that Arthur was completely right.

   C. They said that they had actually given up many times before.

   D. They said that this situation was impossible to fix.

4. **Why had his friends helped Arthur clean out his garage before?**

   A. They wanted Arthur to share his allowance money with them.

   B. They wanted him to come see Galaxy Avengers with them.

   C. Arthur promised to treat them to the dessert that his father would make.

   D. They could use the paint to make interesting pictures.

5. **How had Arthur and his friends taught Buster to multiply?**

   A. They wore the numbers and signs on themselves.

   B. They painted the numbers and signs on a wall in front of him.

   C. They gave him a computer game for math.

   D. They had the Brain teach him after school.

1분에 몇 단어를 읽는지 리딩 속도를 측정해보세요.

$$\frac{647 \ words}{reading \ time \ (\qquad) \ sec} \times 60 = (\qquad) \ WPM$$

Build Your Vocabulary

get it idiom 이해하다
If you say you get it, you become aware of the situation.

get rid of ~ idiom 쫓아버리다, 없애다; ~을 면하다, 벗어나다
When you get rid of something that you do not want or do not like, you take action so that you no longer have it or suffer from it.

‡ **remind** [rimáind] v. 생각나게 하다, 상기시키다, 일깨우다
If someone reminds you of a fact or event that you already know about, they say something which makes you think about it.

pick on idiom (비난하거나 벌을 주면서 부당하게) ~을 괴롭히다
If you pick on someone, you treat them badly or unfairly, especially repeatedly.

‡ **cross** [krɔːs] v. 가로지르다, 건너다; 교차시키다; a. 가로지른; 교차한; n. 십자가
If you cross something such as a room, a road, or an area of land or water, you move or travel to the other side of it.

suburban [səbə́ːrbən] a. 교외의, 교외에 사는; n. 교외 거주자
Suburban means relating to a suburb.

‡ **chase** [tʃeis] v. 쫓아내다, 쫓아버리다; 뒤쫓다, 추적하다; n. 추적, 추격
If you chase someone or something off, you force them to run away by running after them or threatening them.

shelf [ʃelf] n. (pl. shelves) 책꽂이, (책장의) 칸; 선반
A shelf is a flat piece which is attached to a wall or to the sides of a cupboard for keeping books.

satellite [sætilait] n. 위성, 인공위성
A satellite is an object which has been sent into space in order to collect information or to be part of a communications system.

weird [wiə:rd] a. 이상한, 기묘한; 수상한
If you describe something or someone as weird, you mean that they are strange.

scary [skéəri] n. 무서운, 두려운
Something that is scary is rather frightening.

unsuccessful [ʌsəksésfəl] a. 성공하지 못한 (unsuccessfully ad. 실패하여)
Something that is unsuccessful does not achieve what it was intended to achieve.

author [ɔ́:θər] n. 저자, 필자
The author of a piece of writing is the person who wrote it.

comment [kámənt] n. 논평, 의견; v. 논평하다, 의견을 말하다
A comment is something that you say which expresses your opinion of something or which gives an explanation of it.

support [səpɔ́:rt] n. 지지, 받침; v. 지지하다, 유지하다
If you give support to someone during a difficult or unhappy time, you are kind to them and help them.

rally [ræli] n. 집회; v. (원조·지지를 위해) 단결하다
A rally is a large public meeting that is held in order to show support for something such as a political party.

concern [kənsə́:rn] v. 염려하다; ~에 관계하다; 관심을 갖다; n. 염려; 관심
(concerned a. 우려하는)
If something concerns you, it worries you.

* **alert** [ələ́:rt] n. 경계 태세; v. 경보를 발하다; a. 경계하는, 기민한
(red alert n. 적색 경보, 긴급 비상 사태)
If a hospital, a police force, or a military force is on red alert, they have been warned that there may be an emergency, so they can be ready to deal with it.

shout [ʃaut] v. 외치다, 큰 소리 치다
If you shout, you say something very loudly, usually because you want people a long distance away to hear you or because you are angry.

* **scratch** [skrætʃ] v. 긁다, 할퀴다; n. 생채기, 할큄, 찰과상
If you scratch yourself, you rub your fingernails against your skin because it is itching.

generally [dʒénərəli] ad. 일반적으로, 보통
(generally speaking idiom 일반적으로 말해서)
You use generally to say that something happens or is used on most occasions but not on every occasion.

minor [máinər] n. 미성년자; 부전공; a. 작은 쪽의, 중요치 않은
A minor is a person who is still legally a child.

limit [límit] v. 제한하다, 한정하다; n. 제한, 한계 (limited a. 제한된)
If you limit something, you prevent it from becoming greater than a particular amount or degree.

* **access** [ǽkses] n. 접근; v. 접근하다; (컴퓨터에) 접속하다
If you have access to something such as information or equipment, you have the opportunity or right to see it or use it.

legal [líːgəl] a. 법률의, 합법적인 (legal recourse n. 법적 대응책)
Legal is used to describe things that relate to the law.

recourse [ríːkɔːrs] n. (힘든 상황에서 도움을 얻기 위한) 의지
To have recourse to a particular course of action means to have to do that action in order to achieve something.

arbitration [à:rbətréiʃən] n. 조정, 중재
Arbitration is the judging of a dispute between people or groups by someone who is not involved.

be willing to idiom 기꺼이 ~하는, 흔쾌히 ~하다
If someone is willing to do something, they are fairly happy about doing it.

give up idiom 포기하다, 단념하다
If you give up, you decide that you cannot do something and stop trying to do it.

*__garage__ [gərá:dʒ] n. 차고, 주차장
A garage is a building in which you keep a car.

*__galaxy__ [gǽləksi] n. 화려한 대집단; 은하, 은하수
If you talk about a galaxy of people from a particular profession, you mean a group of them who are all famous or important.

avenge [əvéndʒ] v. 복수하다 (avenger n. 복수하는 사람)
If you avenge a wrong or harmful act, you hurt or punish the person who is responsible for it.

*__trash__ [træʃ] n. 쓰레기; v. 부수다, 엉망으로 만들다 (trash bag n. 쓰레기 봉지)
Trash consists of unwanted things or waste material such as used paper, empty containers and bottles, and waste food.

*__stack__ [stæk] v. 쌓다, 쌓아올리다; n. 더미; 많음, 다량
If you stack a number of things, you arrange them in neat piles.

‡__sweep__ [swi:p] v. (빗자루·손 등으로) 쓸다; (거칠게) 휩쓸고 가다; n. 쓸기, 비질하기; 훑음
If you sweep an area of floor or ground, you push dirt or rubbish off it using a brush with a long handle.

‡__balance__ [bǽləns] v. 균형잡다, 균형을 이루다; n. 균형
If you balance something somewhere, or if it balances there, it remains steady and does not fall.

broom [bru:m] n. 비, 빗자루

A broom is a kind of brush with a long handle. You use a broom for sweeping the floor.

knock [nak] v. 부딪치다, 충돌하다; (문을) 두드리다, 노크하다

(knock over idiom 넘어뜨리다, 때려눕히다)

If you knock something, you touch or hit it roughly, especially so that it falls or moves.

spill [spil] v. 엎지르다, 흘리다; n. 엎지름, 유출

If a liquid spills or if you spill it, it accidentally flows over the edge of a container.

startle [sta:rtl] v. 깜짝 놀라게 하다; 움찔하다; n. 깜짝 놀람 (startled a. 놀란)

If something sudden and unexpected startles you, it surprises and frightens you slightly.

drop [drap] v. (물건을) 떨어뜨리다; 똑똑 떨어지다; n. 방울(져 떨어짐)

If you drop something, you accidentally let it fall.

garbage [gá:rbidʒ] n. 쓰레기, 찌꺼기

Garbage is rubbish, especially waste from a kitchen.

tumble [tʌmbl] v. 넘어지다, 굴러 떨어지다; n. 추락; 폭락

If someone or something tumbles somewhere, they fall there with a rolling or bouncing movement.

accident [ǽksidənt] n. 사고, 사건; 우연

If someone has an accident, something unpleasant happens to them that was not intended, sometimes causing injury or death.

make it idiom (바라던 일을) 이룩하다, 성공하다, 해내다; (시간에) 대다

If you make it, you are successful in achieving something difficult, or in surviving through a very difficult period.

bump [bʌmp] n. (도로의) 튀어나온 부분; 혹; v. 덜컹거리며 가다; (쾅 하고) 부딪치다

A bump on a road is a raised, uneven part.

* **math** [mæθ] n. (= mathematics) 수학
Math is the study of numbers, quantities, or shapes.

* **couch** [kautʃ] n. 소파, 긴 의자
A couch is a long, comfortable seat for two or three people.

* **concentrate** [kánsəntrèit] v. 집중하다, 전념하다 (concentration n. 집중)
If you concentrate on something, you give all your attention to it.

* **spread** [spred] v. (spread–spread) 퍼지다, 펴다, 펼치다; 뿌리다; n. 퍼짐
(spread out idiom 널리 퍼지다)
If you spread something somewhere, you open it out or arrange it over
a place or surface, so that all of it can be seen or used easily.

* **chest** [tʃest] ① n. 가슴, 흉부 ② n. 상자, 궤
Your chest is the top part of the front of your body where your ribs,
lungs, and heart are.

* **multiply** [mʌltiplai] v. 곱하다, 늘리다, 증가하다 (multiplication n. 곱셈)
If you multiply one number by another, you add the first number to itself
as many times as is indicated by the second number.

* **symbol** [símbəl] n. 상징, 기호
A symbol of something such as an idea is a shape or design that is used
to represent it.

drape [dreip] v. 우아하게 걸치다, 주름을 잡아 예쁘게 덮다; n. 드리워진 모양, 드레이프
If you drape a piece of cloth somewhere, you place it there so that it
hangs down in a casual and graceful way.

* **equal** [íːkwəl] a. 같은, 동등한; v. ~와 같다 (equal sign n. 등호, = 표시)
If two things are equal or if one thing is equal to another, they are the
same in size, number, standard, or value.

* **forehead** [fɔ́ːrhèd] n. 이마
Your forehead is the area at the front of your head between your
eyebrows and your hair.

itch [itʃ] v. 가렵다, 근질근질하다; n. 가려움
When a part of your body itches, you have an unpleasant feeling on your skin that makes you want to scratch.

strike [straik] n. 파업; 공격, 공습; v. 치다, 찌르다; 습격하다; 충돌하다
When there is a strike, workers stop doing their work for a period of time, usually in order to try to get better pay or conditions for themselves.

sigh [sai] v. 한숨 쉬다; n. 한숨, 탄식
When you sigh, you let out a deep breath, as a way of expressing feelings such as disappointment, tiredness, or pleasure.

fold [fould] v. (손·팔·다리를) 끼다, 포개다; 접다, 접어 포개다
If you fold your arms or hands, you bring them together and cross or link them, for example over your chest.

roll one's eyes idiom 눈을 굴리다
If you roll your eyes, you show with your eyes that you don't believe someone or aren't interested in what they're saying.

worth [wəːrθ] a. ~의 가치가 있는; n. 가치, 값어치
If something is worth a particular action, or if an action is worth doing, it is considered to be important enough for that action.

Chapter 4

1. **Where did Arthur and his friends meet after lunch?**

   A. Arthur's garage

   B. The library

   C. The Sugar Bowl

   D. A bookstore

2. **How do they decide to show that they have support for bringing the books back?**

   A. They decided to collect signatures on a petition.

   B. They decided to hold a rally for the books.

   C. They decided to call Muffy for her support.

   D. They decided to save the Old City Hall building.

3. How did Buster and Arthur start to collect signatures?

A. They offered a chance to swim in their pool.

B. They had Arthur perform a balancing act on his front lawn.

C. They had Arthur dress like a clown and make jokes.

D. They read the scary stories through a loudspeaker.

4. How did Francine and Sue Ellen collect signatures?

A. They gave lemonade to people in the park.

B. They sang songs to children in the park.

C. They played a jump rope game in the park.

D. They asked people on bikes in the park.

5. Why did people sign for the Brain?

A. They wanted to read the scary stories themselves.

B. They wanted him to explain with more details.

C. They wanted him to explain the situation to the bus driver.

D. They wanted him to stop explaining things to them.

Check Your Reading Speed
1분에 몇 단어를 읽는지 리딩 속도를 측정해보세요.

$$\frac{602 \text{ words}}{\text{reading time (} \quad \text{) sec}} \times 60 = (\quad) \text{ WPM}$$

Build Your Vocabulary

quantitative [kwántətèitiv] a. 양적인, 분량의 (quantitatively ad. 양적으로)
Quantitative means relating to different sizes or amounts of things.

*.**demonstrate** [démənstreit] v. 논증하다, 설명하다; 실지로 해보이다
If you demonstrate a particular skill, quality, or feeling, you show by your actions that you have it.

‡**opinion** [əpínjən] n. 의견, 견해
Your opinion about something is what you think or believe about it.

복습**wonder** [wándə:r] v. 호기심을 가지다, 이상하게 여기다; n. 경탄할 만한 것, 경이
If you wonder about something, you think about it because it interests you and you want to know more about it.

take action idiom ~에 대해 조치를 취하다, 행동에 옮기다
If you take action, you start doing something.

*.**signature** [sígnətʃə:r] n. 서명, 사인
Your signature is your name, written in your own characteristic way, often at the end of a document to indicate that you wrote the document.

*.**petition** [pətíʃən] n. 청원(서), 탄원; v. 청원하다, 탄원하다
A petition is a document signed by a lot of people which asks a government or other official group to do a particular thing.

support [səpɔ́:rt] n. 지지, 받침; v. 지지하다, 유지하다
If you give support to someone during a difficult or unhappy time, you are kind to them and help them.

rally [rǽli] n. 집회; v. (원조·지지를 위해) 단결하다
A rally is a large public meeting that is held in order to show support for something such as a political party.

split [split] v. (split-split) 쪼개다, 찢다, 째다; n. 분열
If something splits or if you split it, it is divided into two or more parts.

spread [spred] v. (spread-spread) 퍼지다, 펴다, 펼치다; 뿌리다; n. 퍼짐
(spread out idiom 널리 퍼지다)
If people or things are spread out, they are a long way apart.

team up idiom 한 팀이 되다, 협력하다
If you team up with someone, you work together with them in order to do something.

lawn [lɔ:n] n. 잔디밭, 잔디
A lawn is an area of grass that is kept cut short and is usually part of someone's garden or backyard, or part of a park.

shout [ʃaut] v. 외치다, 큰 소리 치다
If you shout, you say something very loudly, usually because you want people a long distance away to hear you or because you are angry.

megaphone [mégəfoun] n. 확성기; v. 큰 소리로 전하다
A megaphone is a cone-shaped device for making your voice sound louder in the open air.

whiz [hwiz] v. 쌩 하고 지나가다; n. 씽(화살·총알 등이 내는 소리)
If something whizzes somewhere, it moves there very fast.

step up idiom 앞으로 나오다
If you step up, you come forward.

* **amazing** [əméiziŋ] a. (감탄스럽도록) 놀라운, 멋진
You say that something is amazing when it is very surprising and makes you feel pleasure, approval, or wonder.

* **perform** [pərfɔ́:rm] v. 공연하다, 재주를 부리다; 이행하다, 수행하다
If you perform a play, a piece of music, or a dance, you do it in front of an audience.

feat [fi:t] n. 묘기, 재주; 공적, 위업
If you refer to an action, or the result of an action, as a feat, you admire it because it is an impressive and difficult achievement.

* **dive** [daiv] v. 뛰어들다, 잠수하다; 급히 움직이다 (diving mask n. 잠수경)
If you dive into some water, you jump in head-first with your arms held straight above your head.

bathing [béiðiŋ] n. 수영; 목욕 (bathing suit n. 수영복)
A bathing suit is a clothing which people wear when they go swimming.

* **suit** [su:t] n. (특정한 활동 때 입는) ~복, ~옷; 정장
A particular type of suit is a piece of clothing that you wear for a particular activity.

* **balance** [bǽləns] v. 균형잡다, 균형을 이루다; 비교 대조하다; n. 균형
If you balance something somewhere, or if it balances there, it remains steady and does not fall.

inflatable [infléitəbl] a. (공기 등으로) 부풀게 할 수 있는
An inflatable object is one that you fill with air when you want to use it.

wade [weid] v. (물·진흙 속을 힘겹게) 헤치며 걷다 (wading pool n. 어린이의 물놀이터)
If you wade through something that makes it difficult to walk, usually water or mud, you walk through it.

* **commercial** [kəmə́:rʃəl] n. (텔레비전·라디오의) 상업 광고; a. 상업의, 무역의
A commercial is an advertisement that is broadcast on television or radio.

* **whisper** [hwíspə:r] v. 속삭이다; n. 속삭임
When you whisper, you say something very quietly.

attention [əténʃən] n. 주의, 관심; 배려
If you give someone or something your attention, you look at it, listen to it, or think about it carefully.

go ahead idiom (~을) 시작하다, 밀고 나가다
If someone goes ahead with something, they do it, although there may be a problem, or they may have objected or expressed doubts.

breath [breθ] n. 한 번 들이마시기[쉬기]; 숨, 호흡
When you take a breath, you breathe in once.

broom [bru:m] n. 비, 빗자루
A broom is a kind of brush with a long handle. You use a broom for sweeping the floor.

lean [li:n] v. 기울다, (몸을) 숙이다
When you lean in a particular direction, you bend your body in that direction.

twirl [twə:rl] v. 빙빙 돌리다, 빠르게 돌다; n. 회전
If you twirl something or if it twirls, it turns around and around with a smooth, fairly fast movement.

propeller [prəpélər] n. 프로펠러, 추진기
A propeller is a device with blades which is attached to a boat or aircraft. The engine makes the propeller spin round and causes the boat or aircraft to move.

sponsor [spánsər] n. 후원자, 보증인; v. 후원하다, 보증하다
A sponsor is a person or organization that sponsors something or someone.

meanwhile [mí:nwàil] ad. (다른 일이 일어나고 있는) 그 동안에
Meanwhile means while a particular thing is happening.

chant [ʧænt] v. (단조로운 말투로) 반복해 말하다; 일제히 외치다; 노래를 부르다; n. (규칙적으로 반복되는) 문구; 노래
If you chant something or if you chant, you repeat the same words over and over again.

educate [édʒukèit] v. 교육하다; 기르다, 양성하다
To educate people means to teach them better ways of doing something or a better way of living.

passenger [pǽsəndʒər] n. 승객
A passenger in a vehicle such as a bus, boat, or plane is a person who is traveling in it, but who is not driving it or working on it.

blackboard [blǽkbɔ̀:rd] n. 칠판
A blackboard is a dark-colored board that you can write on with chalk.

flow chart [flóu tʃɑ̀:rt] n. 흐름도, 일람표
A flow chart or a flow diagram is a diagram which represents the sequence of actions in a particular process or activity.

equation [ikwéiʒən] n. 등식, 방정식
An equation is a mathematical statement saying that two amounts or values are the same.

predict [pridíkt] v. 예언하다, 예상하다
If you predict an event, you say that it will happen.

impact [ímpækt] n. 영향, 효과; 충격, 충돌; v. 영향을 주다; 충돌하다
The impact that something has on a situation, process, or person is a sudden and powerful effect that it has on them.

geometric [dʒì:əmétrik] a. 기하학적인
Geometric or geometrical patterns or shapes consist of regular shapes or lines.

note [nout] v. ~에 주목[주의]하다; n. 메모, 필기; 편지, 쪽지
If you note a fact, you become aware of it.

marked [ma:rkt] a. 뚜렷한
A marked change or difference is very obvious and easily noticed.

curve [kə:rv] n. 곡선, 곡면; v. 구부러지다, 만곡하다 (learning curve n. 학습 곡선)
You can refer to a change in something as a particular curve, especially when it is represented on a graph.

hypothesis [haipáθəsis] n. 가설, 가정, 추측
A hypothesis is an idea which is suggested as a possible explanation for a particular situation or condition, but which has not yet been proved to be correct.

recreation [rèkriéiʃən] n. 휴양, 기분 전환, 오락 (recreational a. 오락의, 기분 전환의)
Recreation consists of things that you do in your spare time to relax.

yield [ji:ld] v. 산출하다, 생산하다; 넘겨주다, 양도하다; n. 산출
If something yields a result or piece of information, it produces it.

educational [èdʒukéiʃənl] a. 교육(상)의, 교육적인
An educational experience teaches you something.

benefit [bénəfit] n. 혜택, 이득; (모금을 위한) 자선행사; v. 이익을 주다, 이득이 되다
The benefit of something is the help that you get from it or the advantage that results from it.

invite [inváit] v. (정중히) 요구하다, 요청하다; 초청하다, 초대하다
If you are invited to do something, you are formally asked or given permission to do it.

by all means idiom (승낙의 뜻을 강조하여) 아무렴, 좋다마다
By all means is used to say that you are very willing for someone to have something or do something.

agree [əgríː] v. 동의하다, 찬성하다
If you agree with an action or suggestion, you approve of it.

crowd [kraud] v. 모여들다, 붐비다; n. 군중, 인파; 많은 것, 다수
When people crowd around someone or something, they gather closely together around them.

clipboard [klípbɔ̀ːrd] n. 클립보드(집게가 달린 필기판)
A clipboard is a board with a clip at the top.

after all idiom (예상과는 달리) 결국에는; 어쨌든
After all is used to show that something is the opposite of what you first intend to do or expect to happen.

1. **Where did Arthur and Buster go to next after their neighborhood to find signatures?**
   A. The school
   B. The pool
   C. The TV station
   D. The park

2. **What do Arthur and Buster decide to do in the park?**
   A. They decided to do the Amazing Arthur act again.
   B. They decided to jump rope with Francine and Sue Ellen.
   C. They decided to split up and ask people for signatures.
   D. They decided to hold a rally for the Scare-Your-Pants-Off Club books.

3. What was the old woman doing in the park?

   A. She was jogging.

   B. She was biking.

   C. She was rollerblading.

   D. She was gardening.

4. What did Arthur's father say reading different things was like?

   A. He said it was healthy like the food groups.

   B. He said it was fun like music genres.

   C. He said it was important like exercising.

   D. He said it was confusing like the news.

5. What did the woman forget when she left?

   A. She forgot her gardening tools.

   B. She forgot to sign the petition.

   C. She forgot her glasses.

   D. She forgot to clean up.

Check Your Reading Speed

1분에 몇 단어를 읽는지 리딩 속도를 측정해보세요.

$$\frac{447 \ words}{reading \ time \ (\quad) \ sec} \times 60 = (\quad) \ WPM$$

Build Your Vocabulary

collect [kəlékt] v. 모으다, 수집하다; 모금하다
If you collect a number of things, you bring them together from several places or from several people.

signature [sígnətʃəːr] n. 서명, 사인
Your signature is your name, written in your own characteristic way, often at the end of a document to indicate that you wrote the document.

neighborhood [néibərhùd] n. 근처, 이웃; 이웃 사람들
A neighborhood is one of the parts of a town where people live.

gather [gǽðər] v. 모으다, 끌다; 모이다, 집결하다
If people gather somewhere or if someone gathers people somewhere, they come together in a group.

amazing [əméiziŋ] a. (감탄스럽도록) 놀라운, 멋진
You say that something is amazing when it is very surprising and makes you feel pleasure, approval, or wonder.

split [split] v. 쪼개다, 찢다, 째다; n. 분열
If something splits or if you split it, it is divided into two or more parts.

pond [pand] n. (인공으로 만든) 연못
A pond is a small area of water that is smaller than a lake.

set out idiom 출발하다, 떠나다
If you set out, you leave a place and begin a journey, especially a long journey.

catch up with idiom 따라잡다
If you catch up with someone or something, you reach them ahead of you by going faster than them.

catch me later idiom 안녕, 나중에 이야기합시다
People say 'catch me later' for saying goodbye, especially when they are just about to go somewhere else.

discourage [diskə́:ridʒ] v. 낙담시키다, 실망시키다 (**discouraging** a. 실망스러운)
If someone or something discourages you, they cause you to lose your enthusiasm about your actions.

spot [spat] v. 발견하다, 분별하다; n. 반점, 얼룩; 장소, 지점
If you spot something or someone, you notice them.

tend [tend] v. 돌보다, 보살피다; (~하는) 경향이 있다
If you tend someone or something, you do what is necessary to keep them in a good condition or to improve their condition.

plant [plænt] n. 식물, 초목; 공장; v. (나무·씨앗 등을) 심다
A plant is a living thing that grows in the earth and has a stem, leaves, and roots.

fountain [fáuntən] n. 분수; 샘
A fountain is an ornamental feature in a pool or lake which consists of a long narrow stream of water that is forced up into the air.

be on the move idiom (이리저리로) 옮겨[이동해] 다니다
If you are on the move, you are going from one place to another.

introduce [intrədjú:s] v. 소개하다; 받아들이다, 도입하다
If you introduce yourself to someone, you tell them your name.

perch [pə:rtʃ] v. (높은 곳에) 놓다, 앉히다; n. (새의) 횃대; 높은 자리
To perch somewhere means to be on the top or edge of something.

permission [pəːrmíʃən] n. 허락, 허가, 승인
If someone is given permission to do something, they are allowed to do it.

hesitate [hézətèit] v. 주저하다, 머뭇거리다, 망설이다
If you hesitate, you do not speak or act for a short time, usually because you are uncertain, embarrassed, or worried about what you are going to say or do.

cause [kɔːz] n. 대의 명분, 목적; 원인, 동기; v. 원인이 되다
(for a good cause idiom 대의 명분을 위하여)
If you say that something is for a good cause, you mean that it is worth doing or giving to because it will help other people, for example by raising money for charity.

remove [rimúːv] v. 치우다, 제거하다; 이동하다, 떠나다
If you remove something from a place, you take it away.

petition [pətíʃən] n. 청원(서), 탄원; v. 청원하다, 탄원하다
A petition is a document signed by a lot of people which asks a government or other official group to do a particular thing.

pause [pɔːz] v. 중단하다, 잠시 멈추다; n. 멈춤, 중지
If you pause while you are doing something, you stop for a short period and then continue.

volunteer [vàləntíər] n. 지원자; v. 자진하다, 자발적으로 나서다
(volunteer work n. 자원봉사)
A volunteer is someone who does work without being paid for it, because they want to do it.

depend [dipénd] v. ~에 좌우되다, 달려있다; 의존하다, 의지하다
If you say that one thing depends on another, you mean that the first thing will be affected or determined by the second.

go against idiom 반대하다, 거스르다
If you go against someone or something, you resist or oppose them, acting in a different way from whay they tells you or advises you to do.

healthy [hélθi] a. 건강한, 건강에 좋은
Something that is healthy is good for your health.

bit [bit] n. 조금, 약간; 작은 조각, 한 조각
A bit means to a small extent or degree.

advice [ædváis] n. 충고, 조언
If you give someone advice, you tell them what you think they should do in a particular situation.

heel [hi:l] n. 뒤꿈치; 발; 뒤축
(sit back on one's heel idiom 무릎을 꿇어 엉덩이를 뒤꿈치 위에 오도록 해서 앉다)
Your heel is the back part of your foot, just below your ankle.

miss [mis] v. ~을 빠뜨리다; (어디에 참석하지 않아서 그 일을) 놓치다; (치거나 잡거나 닿지 못하고) 놓치다
If you miss something, you do not include it either deliberately or by accident.

single [síŋgl] a. 단 하나의
You use single to emphasize that you are referring to one thing, and no more than one thing.

frown [fraun] v. 얼굴[눈살]을 찌푸리다; n. 찡그림, 찌푸림
When someone frowns, their eyebrows become drawn together, because they are annoyed or puzzled.

serious [síəriəs] a. 심각한; 중요한, 중대한; 진지한
Serious problems or situations are very bad and cause people to be worried or afraid.

garden [ga:rdn] v. 정원을 가꾸다, 원예를 하다; n. 정원, 뜰 (gardening n. 원예)
If you garden, you do work in your garden such as weeding or planting.

tool [tu:l] n. 도구, 연장
A tool is any instrument or simple piece of equipment that you hold in your hands and use to do a particular kind of work.

^{복습}**give up** idiom 포기하다, 단념하다
If you give up, you decide that you cannot do something and stop trying to do it.

_***puzzle** [pʌzl] v. 곤혹스럽게 하다, 난처하게 하다; n. 수수께끼, 어려운 문제
(puzzled a. 어리둥절한)
If something puzzles you, you do not understand it and feel confused.

^{복습}**clipboard** [klípbɔ̀ːrd] n. 클립보드(집게가 달린 필기판)
A clipboard is a board with a clip at the top.

Chapter 6

1. **How did Arthur feel about the signatures?**

    A. He thought that PAWS would not listen.

    B. He thought they needed more names.

    C. He thought they had enough names.

    D. He thought that they only needed important people to sign.

2. **What news did Muffy have for Arthur and his friends?**

    A. Her parents invited them to a party at WonderWorld.

    B. Her parents were only taking Muffy to WonderWorld.

    C. WonderWorld was closing soon and had a free event.

    D. Her parents were helping bring back the Scare-Your-Pants-Off Club books.

3. **How did Muffy react to seeing the Brain?**
   A. She yelled at him.
   B. She had been waiting for him.
   C. She said hello and smiled.
   D. She just looked at the sidewalk.

4. **Who was responsible for PAWS and the book ban?**
   A. Muffy
   B. Muffy's parents
   C. Muffy's teachers
   D. The Brain

5. **What choice did Muffy give her friends?**
   A. They had to decide between WonderWorld and homework.
   B. They had to decide between WonderWorld and their friendship.
   C. They had to decide between WonderWorld and the books.
   D. They had to decide between the books and their friendship.

Check Your Reading Speed

1분에 몇 단어를 읽는지 리딩 속도를 측정해보세요.

$$\frac{505 \text{ words}}{\text{reading time ( ) sec}} \times 60 = (\quad) \text{ WPM}$$

Build Your Vocabulary

collect [kəlékt] v. 모으다, 수집하다; 모금하다
If you collect a number of things, you bring them together from several places or from several people.

signature [sígnətʃə:r] n. 서명, 사인
Your signature is your name, written in your own characteristic way, often at the end of a document to indicate that you wrote the document.

lick [lik] v. 핥다; n. 한 번 핥기, 핥아먹기
When people or animals lick something, they move their tongue across its surface.

drip [drip] n. 방울져 떨어지는 것, (물)방울; v. 방울방울[똑똑] 떨어지다
A drip is a small individual drop of a liquid.

wonder [wʌndə:r] v. 호기심을 가지다, 이상하게 여기다; n. 경탄할 만한 것, 경이
If you wonder about something, you think about it because it interests you and you want to know more about it.

be supposed to ~ idiom (관습·법·의무로) ~하기로 되어 있다
If you are supposed to do something, you are expected or required to do something according to a rule, a custom or an arrangement.

announce [ənáuns] v. 알리다, 공고하다, 전하다
If you announce a piece of news or an intention, especially something that people may not like, you say it loudly and clearly, so that everyone you are with can hear it.

pause [pɔːz] v. 중단하다, 잠시 멈추다; n. 멈춤, 중지
If you pause while you are doing something, you stop for a short period and then continue.

invite [inváit] v. 초청하다, 초대하다; (정중히) 요구하다, 요청하다
If you invite someone to something such as a party or a meal, you ask them to come to it.

carnival [káːrnəvəl] n. 축제; 서커스; 사육제
A carnival is a traveling show which is held in a park or field and at which there are machines to ride on, entertainments, and games.

theme [θiːm] n. 주제, 테마; a. 특정 분위기를 살린 (theme park n. 테마 파크)
A theme park is a large outdoor area where people pay to go to enjoy themselves.

treat [triːt] n. 특별한 선물, 대접; v. 치료하다, 처치하다; 대하다
If you give someone a treat, you buy or arrange something special for them which they will enjoy.

terrific [tərífik] a. 굉장한, 엄청난; 무서운, 소름이 끼치는
If you describe something or someone as terrific, you are very pleased with them or very impressed by them.

count [kaunt] v. 포함시키다; 세다, 계산하다; 중요하다; n. 계산, 셈
If you count all the things in a group, you add them up in order to find how many there are.

notice [nóutis] v. 알아차리다, 주의하다; n. 통지, 통보; 주의, 주목
If you notice something or someone, you become aware of them.

eye [ai] v. (탐이 나거나 의심스러워) 쳐다보다; n. (한쪽) 눈
If you eye someone or something in a particular way, you look at them carefully in that way.

hold out idiom 내밀다, 뻗다
To hold out means to hold something such as your hand or something in your hand, in front of you toward someone else.

fat [fæt] n. 지방, 기름기; a. 기름기가 많은; 살찐, 뚱뚱한
Fat is a substance contained in foods such as meat, cheese, and butter which forms an energy store in your body.

clutch [klʌʧ] v. 부여잡다, 꽉 잡다, 붙들다; n. 붙잡음, 움켜쥠
If you clutch at something or clutch something, you hold it tightly, usually because you are afraid or anxious.

sidewalk [sáidwɔ́ːk] n. (포장한) 보도, 인도
A sidewalk is a path with a hard surface by the side of a road.

glance [glæns] v. 흘낏 보다, 잠깐 보다; n. 흘낏 봄
If you glance at something or someone, you look at them very quickly and then look away again immediately.

direction [dirékʃən] n. 방향; 지도, 지시
A direction is the general line that someone or something is moving or pointing in.

article [áːrtikl] n. 기사, 논설
An article is a piece of writing that is published in a newspaper or magazine.

ban [bæn] n. 금지(령); 추방; v. 금지하다
A ban is an official ruling that something must not be done, shown, or used.

interview [íntərvjùː] n. 인터뷰; 면접; v. 취재 방문하다; 면접하다
An interview is a conversation in which a journalist puts questions to someone such as a famous person or politician.

skip [skip] v. 건너뛰다, 생략하다; 뛰어다니다, 깡충깡충 뛰다
If you skip or skip over a part of something you are reading or a story you are telling, you miss it out or pass over it quickly and move on to something else.

harm [haːrm] n. 해, 손해; v. 해치다, 손상을 입히다
Harm is the damage to something which is caused by a particular course of action.

awful [ɔ́ːfəl] a. 무서운; 지독한, 대단한
If you say that something is awful, you mean that it is extremely unpleasant, shocking, or bad.

nightmare [náitmɛər] n. 악몽
A nightmare is a very frightening dream.

crack [kræk] n. 갈라진 금; 갑작스런 날카로운 소리; v. 금이 가다, 깨다
A crack is a line that appears on the surface of something when it is slightly damaged.

rally [ræli] n. 집회; v. (원조·지지를 위해) 단결하다
A rally is a large public meeting that is held in order to show support for something such as a political party.

concern [kənsɔ́ːrn] v. 염려하다; ~에 관계하다; 관심을 갖다; n. 염려; 관심
(concerned a. 우려하는)
If something concerns you, it worries you.

afterward [ǽftərwərd] ad. 나중에, 그 후에
If you do something or if something happens afterward, you do it or it happens after a particular event or time that has already been mentioned.

support [səpɔ́ːrt] v. 지지하다, 유지하다; n. 지지, 받침 (supporter n. 지지자)
If you support someone or their ideas or aims, you agree with them, and perhaps help them because you want them to succeed.

celebrate [séləbrèit] v. 기념하다, 축하하다 (celebration n. 축하, 기념)
If you celebrate, you do something enjoyable because of a special occasion.

shock [ʃak] v. 충격을 주다, 놀라게 하다; n. 충격, 쇼크 (shocked a. 충격을 받은)
If something shocks you, it makes you feel very upset, because it involves death or suffering and because you had not expected it.

bite [bait] v. (bit-bitten) 물다, 물어뜯다; n. 물기, 물어뜯기; 한 입(의 분량)
If you bite something, you use your teeth to cut into it, for example in order to eat it or break it.

any old idiom 아무런, 어떤 ~이라도 (상관없는)
You use any old to emphasize that the quality or type of something is not important.

shrug [ʃrʌg] v. (어깨를) 으쓱하다; n. (양 손바닥을 내보이면서 어깨를) 으쓱하기
If you shrug, you raise your shoulders to show that you are not interested in something or that you do not know or care about something.

technical [téknikəl] a. 구체적인; 전문적인, 기술상의
Technical language involves using special words to describe the details of a specialized activity.

hesitate [hézətèit] v. 주저하다, 머뭇거리다, 망설이다
If you hesitate, you do not speak or act for a short time, usually because you are uncertain, embarrassed, or worried about what you are going to say or do.

breath [breθ] n. 숨, 호흡; 한 번 들이마시기[쉬기]
(take a deep breath idiom 심호흡하다)
Your breath is the air that you let out through your mouth when you breathe.

fold [fould] v. (손·팔·다리를) 끼다, 포개다; 접다, 접어 포개다
If you fold your arms or hands, you bring them together and cross or link them, for example over your chest.

bunch [bʌntʃ] n. 다량; 다발, 송이; 떼, 한패
A bunch of things is a number of things, especially a large number.

silly [síli] a. 어리석은, 바보 같은
If you say that someone or something is silly, you mean that they are foolish, childish, or ridiculous.

choice [tʃɔis] n. 선택(권), 선정
Your choice is someone or something that you choose from a range of things.

Chapter 7

1. How did D.W. feel about Arthur's situation?

   A. She thought that it was a hard decision.

   B. She thought that the books were more important.

   C. She thought that he should go to WonderWorld.

   D. She thought she could go to WonderWorld instead of Arthur.

2. What did Mrs. Read tell Arthur about his decision?

   A. He had to do what was right even if it means a sacrifice.

   B. He had to do what was the most fun for him.

   C. He had to do what his mother tells him to do.

   D. He should let D.W. go to WonderWorld instead of him.

3. Why was Mr. Read wearing a clown costume?

A. He worked as a clown in a circus.

B. He was trying to cheer Arthur up by telling him jokes.

C. He was helping with a children's hospital benefit.

D. He was going to surprise D.W. for her birthday.

4. What did Mr. Read tell Arthur when he worried about being the only one to protest PAWS?

A. He told Arthur to try dressing like a clown too.

B. He told Arthur that he could find new friends to help him protest.

C. He told Arthur that he could not be afraid of looking foolish.

D. He told Arthur that he already looked foolish.

5. What did Mr. Read tell Arthur about how clowns work?

A. He told Arthur that clowns always worked for free.

B. He told Arthur that clowns never worked alone.

C. He told Arthur that clowns were sometimes sad.

D. He told Arthur that clowns sometimes worked as a team.

Check Your Reading Speed

1분에 몇 단어를 읽는지 리딩 속도를 측정해보세요.

$$\frac{584 \text{ words}}{\text{reading time ( ) sec}} \times 60 = (\quad) \text{ WPM}$$

Build Your Vocabulary

☀ **complicated** [kámplikèitid] a. 복잡한, 이해하기 어려운
If you say that something is complicated, you mean it has so many parts or aspects that it is difficult to understand or deal with.

복습 **balance** [bǽləns] v. 비교 대조하다; 균형잡다, 균형을 이루다; n. 균형
If you balance one thing with something different, each of the things has the same strength or importance.

☀ **scale** [skeil] ① n. 저울, 저울 접시; n. 규모; 비례, 비율 ② v. 기어오르다 ③ n. 비늘
Scales are a piece of equipment used for weighing things, for example for weighing amounts of food that you need in order to make a particular meal.

creepy [krí:pi] a. 소름이 끼치는, 오싹한; 꾸물꾸물 움직이는
If you say that something or someone is creepy, you mean they make you feel very nervous or frightened.

☀ **lower** [louər] v. 낮추다, 내리다; 줄다, 낮아지다
If you lower something, you move it slowly downward.

☀ **knee** [ni:] n. 무릎
Your knee is the place where your leg bends.

☀☀ **shoot** [ʃu:t] v. (shot-shot) 잽싸게 움직이다; 쏘다, 발사하다
If someone or something shoots in a particular direction, they move in that direction quickly and suddenly.

contest [kántest] n. 경쟁; 논쟁; v. 겨루다, 다투다; 논쟁하다
(no contest idiom 승패는 빤하다)
A contest is a competition or game in which people try to win.

throw up idiom 토하다, 먹은 것을 게우다
If you throw up, you bring food you have eaten back out of your mouth.

and everything idiom 등등, 이것저것 다
And everything means and so on, or and other similar things.

playpen [pléipèn] n. (울타리로 둘러싸인) 어린이 놀이터
A playpen is a small structure which is designed for a baby or young child to play safely in, which has bars or a net round the sides.

break [breik] n. (작업 중의) 휴식; 단절; 틈; v. 깨뜨리다, 부수다; 어기다
A break is a short period of time when you have a rest or a change from what you are doing.

come about idiom (일이) 일어나다, 생기다
If something comes about, it takes place or happens.

sigh [sai] v. 한숨 쉬다; n. 한숨, 탄식
When you sigh, you let out a deep breath, as a way of expressing feelings such as disappointment, tiredness, or pleasure.

miss [mis] v. (어디에 참석하지 않아서 그 일을) 놓치다; (치거나 잡거나 닿지 못하고) 놓치다; ~을 빠뜨리다
If you miss something such as a meeting or an activity, you do not go to it or take part in it.

support [səpɔ́:rt] v. 지지하다, 유지하다; n. 지지, 받침
If you support someone or their ideas or aims, you agree with them, and perhaps help them because you want them to succeed.

nod [nad] v. (고개를) 끄덕이다, 끄덕여 나타내다; n. (고개를) 끄덕임
If you nod, you move your head downward and upward to show agreement, understanding, or approval.

sheet [ʃiːt] n. 한 장의 종이; (침대) 시트 (**balance sheet** n. 대차대조표, 재정증명서)
A sheet of paper is a rectangular piece of paper.

sacrifice [sǽkrəfàis] n. 희생; v. 희생하다, 제물로 바치다
Sacrifice is the act of giving up something that is valuable or important, usually to obtain something else for yourself or for other people.

wander [wándər] v. 돌아다니다, 걸어다니다; 방황하다, 헤메다
If you wander in a place, you walk around there in a casual way, often without intending to go in any particular direction.

stick up for idiom ~을 변호하다, 지지하다
If you stick up for someone or something, you support or defend them when they are being criticized.

mutter [mʌ́tər] v. 중얼거리다, 불평하다; n. 중얼거림, 불평
If you mutter, you speak very quietly so that you cannot easily be heard, often because you are complaining about something.

garage [gərɑ́ːdʒ] n. 차고, 주차장
A garage is a building in which you keep a car.

catering [kéitəriŋ] n. (행사·연회 등을 대상으로 하는) 음식 공급
Catering is the activity of providing food and drink for a large number of people, for example at weddings and parties.

agree [əgríː] v. 동의하다, 찬성하다
If you agree with an action or suggestion, you approve of it.

clown [klaun] n. 어릿광대, 익살꾼
A clown is a performer in a circus who wears funny clothes and bright make-up, and does silly things in order to make people laugh.

costume [kástjuːm] n. 의상, 옷차림
An actor's costume is the set of clothes they wear while they are performing.

benefit [bénəfit] n. (모금을 위한) 자선행사; 혜택, 이득; v. 이익을 주다, 이득이 되다
A benefit, or a benefit concert or dinner, is an event that is held in order to raise money for a particular charity or person.

protest [próutest] v. 항의하다, 이의를 제기하다; n. 항의
If you protest against something or about something, you say or show publicly that you object to it.

adjust [ədʒʌst] v. (옷매무새 등을) 바로 하다, 조정하다; 적응하다; 조절하다
If you adjust something such as your clothing or a machine, you correct or alter its position or setting.

bald [bɔːld] a. (머리 등이) 벗겨진, 대머리의; v. 머리가 벗겨지다
Someone who is bald has little or no hair on the top of their head.

wig [wig] n. 가발; 머리 장식
A wig is a covering of false hair which you wear on your head.

afraid [əfréid] a. 두려워하는, 걱정하는; ~할 용기가 없는
If you are afraid of someone or afraid to do something, you are frightened because you think that something very unpleasant is going to happen to you.

foolish [fúːliʃ] a. 어리석은, 바보같은
If someone's behavior or action is foolish, it is not sensible and shows a lack of good judgment.

rubber [rʌ́bər] a. 고무의; n. 고무
Rubber things are made of a strong, waterproof, elastic substance.

wonder [wʌ́ndər] v. 호기심을 가지다, 이상하게 여기다; n. 경탄할 만한 것, 경이
If you wonder about something, you think about it because it interests you and you want to know more about it.

stare [stɛər] v. 응시하다, 뚫어지게 보다
If you stare at someone or something, you look at them for a long time.

suit [suːt] n. (특정한 활동 때 입는) ~복, ~옷; 정장

A particular type of suit is a piece of clothing that you wear for a particular activity.

bunch [bʌntʃ] n. 떼, 한패; 다발, 송이; 다량

A bunch of people is a group of people who share one or more characteristics or who are doing something together.

imaginary [imǽdʒənèri] a. 상상의, 가공의

An imaginary person, place, or thing exists only in your mind or in a story, and not in real life.

spotlight [spálàit] n. 스포트라이트, (세상의) 주시, 주목

A spotlight is a powerful light, for example in a theater, which can be directed so that it lights up a small area.

(all) by oneself idiom 혼자 힘으로, 혼자서

If you do something all by yourself, you do it alone, without anyone else or any help.

bow [bau] ① n. (고개 숙여 하는) 인사, 절; v. 머리를 숙이다, 굽히다 ② n. 활; 곡선

When you take a bow to someone, you briefly bend your body toward them as a formal way of greeting them or showing respect.

Chapter

8

1. **How did Muffy act in front of the library with her parents?**

A. She kept smiling at her friends.

B. She kept trying to hide behind her parents.

C. She kept shouting over her parents' words.

D. She kept trying to apologize to her friends.

2. **Why did Mr. Crosswire say he was holding the rally?**

A. He wanted parents to become closer to each other.

B. He cared about the children's schoolwork.

C. He wanted children to stop reading all books.

D. He cared about Muffy and the other children.

3. Why were Arthur's friends late to the library?

   A. They had been busy watching TV.

   B. They had been buying signs for the protest.

   C. They had been collecting more signatures.

   D. They had been hesitating over whether to come.

4. What did his friends decide Arthur should do?

   A. They decided that Arthur should give the signatures to Mr. Crosswire.

   B. They decided that Arthur should ask Mr. Crosswire to help him.

   C. They decided that Arthur should perform Amazing Arthur in front of the crowd.

   D. They decided that Arthur should give the books to Mr. Crosswire.

5. What question was Mr. Crosswire asked from the crowd?

   A. He was asked if he had bought the Scare-Your-Pants-Off Club books.

   B. He was asked if he had read the Scare-Your-Pants-Off Club books.

   C. He was asked if he had heard of the Scare-Your-Pants-Off Club books.

   D. He was asked if he had written the Scare-Your-Pants-Off Club books.

1분에 몇 단어를 읽는지 리딩 속도를 측정해보세요.

$$\frac{493 \ words}{reading \ time \ (\qquad) \ sec} \times 60 = (\qquad) \ WPM$$

Build Your Vocabulary

duck [dʌk] ① v. (머리나 몸을) 휙 숙이다, 피하다, 급히 움직이다 ② n. 오리
If you duck, you move your head or the top half of your body quickly downward to avoid something that might hit you, or to avoid being seen.

crowd [kraud] n. 많은 것, 다수; 군중, 인파; v. 모여들다, 붐비다
A crowd is a large group of people who have gathered together, for example to watch or listen to something interesting, or to protest about something.

gather [gǽðər] v. 모으다, 끌다; 모이다, 집결하다
If people gather somewhere or if someone gathers people somewhere, they come together in a group.

portable [pɔ́:rtəbl] a. 휴대용의, 들고 다닐 수 있는
A portable machine or device is designed to be easily carried or moved.

microphone [máikrəfòun] n. 마이크(로폰)
A microphone is a device that is used to make sounds louder or to record them on a tape recorder.

cheer [ʧiər] n. 환호(성); v. 환호성을 지르다, 응원하다
A cheer is a shout of encouragement, approval or congratulation.

polite [pəláit] a. 예의 바른, 공손한
Someone who is polite has good manners and behaves in a way that is socially correct and not rude to other people.

applause [əplɔ́ːz] n. 박수 (갈채)
Applause is the noise made by a group of people clapping their hands to show approval.

paw [pɔː] n. (동물·갈고리 발톱이 있는) 발; v. 앞발로 차다
The paws of an animal such as a cat, dog, or bear are its feet, which have claws for gripping things and soft pads for walking on.

attention [əténʃən] n. 주의, 관심; 배려 (pay attention idiom 관심을 갖다)
If you give someone or something your attention, you look at it, listen to it, or think about it carefully.

obey [oubéi] v. 복종하다, 따르다
If you obey a person, a command, or an instruction, you do what you are told to do.

law [lɔː] n. 법, 법률
law is a system of rules that a society or government develops in order to deal with crime, business agreements, and social relationships.

close the book on ~ idiom (수사를) 그만두다, 중단하다
If you close the book on something, you stop doing it because you no longer believe you will be successful or will find a solution.

wonder [wʌ́ndər] v. 호기심을 가지다, 이상하게 여기다; n. 경탄할 만한 것, 경이
If you wonder about something, you think about it because it interests you and you want to know more about it.

signature [sígnətʃəːr] n. 서명, 사인
Your signature is your name, written in your own characteristic way, often at the end of a document to indicate that you wrote the document.

hold out idiom 내밀다, 뻗다
To hold out means to hold something such as your hand or something in your hand, in front of you toward someone else.

petition [pətíʃən] n. 청원(서), 탄원; v. 청원하다, 탄원하다
A petition is a document signed by a lot of people which asks a government or other official group to do a particular thing.

sheet [ʃiːt] n. 한 장의 종이; (침대) 시트
A sheet of paper is a rectangular piece of paper.

dozen [dʌzn] n. (pl.) 수십, 다수; 12개
If you refer to dozens of things or people, you are emphasizing that there are very many of them.

breath [breθ] n. 한 번 들이마시기, 한 번 쉬기; 숨, 호흡
(take a deep breath idiom 심호흡하다)
When you take a breath, you breathe in once.

haunt [hɔːnt] v. (유령이) 출몰하다; (생각 따위가) 계속 떠오르다, 늘 따라다니다
(haunted a. 유령이 자주 나오는)
A ghost or spirit that haunts a place or a person regularly appears in the place, or is seen by the person and frightens them.

miss [mis] v. (어디에 참석하지 않아서 그 일을) 놓치다; (치거나 잡거나 닿지 못하고) 놓치다; ~을 빠뜨리다
If you miss something such as a meeting or an activity, you do not go to it or take part in it.

take a stand idiom 태도를 취하다
If you take or make a stand, you do something or say something in order to make it clear what your attitude to a particular thing is.

fail [feil] v. 실패하다, ~하지 못하다; 도움을 못 주다, 실망시키다
If you fail to do something that you were trying to do, you are unable to do it or do not succeed in doing it.

on a roll idiom 승승장구 하고 있다
If you are on a roll, you are experiencing a period of success at what you are doing.

that's just it idiom 바로 그것[그 점]이 문제이다
People say 'that's just it' to indicate that is exactly the problem.

roll [roul] v. 굴리다; 구르다, 굴러가다[오다]; n. 굴리기, 던지기; 통, 두루마리
When something rolls or when you roll it, it moves along a surface, turning over many times.

right [rait] n. 권리; 정당성, 올바름; 오른쪽; a. 옳은, 바른; ad. 정확히, 바로, 꼭
Your rights are what you are morally or legally entitled to do or to have.

fair [fɛər] ① a. 타당한, 온당한; 공정한, 공평한 ② n. 축제 마당; 박람회, 품평회
Something or someone that is fair is reasonable, right, and just.

support [səpɔ́:rt] n. 지지, 받침; v. 지지하다, 유지하다
If you give support to someone during a difficult or unhappy time, you are kind to them and help them.

admire [ædmáiər] v. 감탄하며 바라보다; 존경하다, 칭찬하다
If you admire someone or something, you like and respect them very much.

spirit [spírit] n. 열성, 용기; 정신; v. ~의 기운을 북돋우다
Spirit is the courage and determination that helps people to survive in difficult times and to keep their way of life and their beliefs.

good [gud] n. 이점, 이익; 선, 미덕; a. 좋은, 친절한
If something is done for the good of a person or organization, it is done in order to benefit them.

capital [kǽpətl] n. 대문자; 자본, 자산; 수도, 중심지; a. 자본의; 주요한
Capitals or capital letters are written or printed letters in the form which is used at the beginning of sentences or names.

familiar [fəmíljər] a. 친숙한, 잘 알고 있는; 친한; 잘 알려진
If someone or something is familiar to you, you recognize them or know them well.

surprising [sərpráiziŋ] a. 놀라운, 놀랄 만한 (surprisingly ad. 놀랍게도)
Something that is surprising is unexpected or unusual and makes you feel surprised.

confuse [kənfjú:z] v. 어리둥절하게 하다, 혼동하다 (confused a. 당황한, 어리둥절한)
To confuse someone means to make it difficult for them to know exactly what is happening or what to do.

Chapter 9

1. **How did Mr. Crosswire know the old woman that Arthur had spoken with in the park?**

   A. She was his grade-school English teacher.

   B. She was his grade-school English tutor.

   C. She was his mother's grade-school friend.

   D. She was his gardener.

2. **How did Miss McWord say that each story was like a seed?**

   A. They were a part of nature and grew like trees.

   B. They could grow into a desire to read more books.

   C. They could grow into a passion for writing more stories.

   D. They could grow and expand a child's knowledge of many things.

3. Why was Miss McWord so knowledgeable about writers?

A. Her best friend was the author of the Scare-Your-Pants-Off Club books.

B. She was a fine English teacher and had met many authors.

C. She had taught many children how to write stories.

D. She was the author of the Scare-Your-Pants-Off Club books.

4. What was the real reason for Muffy's nightmare?

A. She had read one of the Scare-Your-Pants-Off Club books before bed.

B. She had been told a scary ghost story by her father before bed.

C. She had eaten a quart of ice cream before bed.

D. She had watched a scary movie before bed.

5. Why did Mr. Crosswire think listening to a Scare-Your-Pants-Off Club story was an excellent idea?

A. Anything was better than facing his wife.

B. Muffy wanted him to hear one of the stories.

C. He enjoyed scary stories.

D. He wanted to apologize to Miss McWord.

Check Your Reading Speed

1분에 몇 단어를 읽는지 리딩 속도를 측정해보세요.

$$\frac{604 \text{ words}}{\text{reading time ( ) sec}} \times 60 = (\quad) \text{ WPM}$$

Build Your Vocabulary

crowd [kraud] n. 군중, 인파; 많은 것, 다수; v. 모여들다, 붐비다
A crowd is a large group of people who have gathered together, for example to watch or listen to something interesting, or to protest about something.

condemn [kəndém] v. 규탄하다, 비난하다; 선고를 내리다
If you condemn something, you say that it is very bad and unacceptable.

pull back idiom 물러서다, 뒷걸음질치다; 후퇴하다
If you pull back, you move backward away from someone or something.

reveal [riví:l] v. 나타내다, 보이다; 폭로하다, 밝히다
If you reveal something that has been out of sight, you uncover it so that people can see it.

recognize [rékəgnàiz] v. 인지하다, 알아보다; 인정하다
If you recognize someone or something, you know who that person is or what that thing is.

throat [θrout] n. 목구멍; 목 (clear one's throat idiom 목을 가다듬다, 헛기침하다)
Your throat is the back of your mouth and the top part of the tubes that go down into your stomach and your lungs.

sigh [sai] v. 한숨 쉬다; n. 한숨, 탄식
When you sigh, you let out a deep breath, as a way of expressing feelings such as disappointment, tiredness, or pleasure.

surprise [sərpráiz] v. 놀라게 하다, 경악하게 하다 (surprised a. 매우 놀란)
If you surprise someone, you give them, tell them, or do something they are not expecting.

startle [sta:rtl] v. 깜짝 놀라게 하다; 움찔하다; n. 깜짝 놀람 (startled a. 놀란)
If something sudden and unexpected startles you, it surprises and frightens you slightly.

memory [méməri] n. 기억(력), 회상
Your memory is your ability to remember things.

fail [feil] v. 도움을 못 주다, 실망시키다; 실패하다, ~하지 못하다
If a quality or ability that you have fails you, or if it fails, it is not good enough in a particular situation to enable you to do what you want to do.

common sense [kámən sens] n. 상식(적 판단), 분별력
Your common sense is your natural ability to make good judgments and to behave in a practical and sensible way.

assure [əʃúər] v. 보증하다, 확신하다, 단언하다
If you assure someone that something is true or will happen, you tell them that it is definitely true or will definitely happen, often in order to make them less worried.

bit [bit] n. 작은 조각, 한 조각; 조금, 약간 (every bit idiom 전적으로, 아주)
You say that one thing is every bit as good, interesting, or important as another to emphasize that the first thing is just as good, interesting, or important as the second.

admit [ædmít] v. 인정하다
If you admit that something bad, unpleasant, or embarrassing is true, you agree, often unwillingly, that it is true.

appreciate [əprí:ʃièit] v. 진가를 알아보다[인정하다]; 고마워하다; 환영하다
If you appreciate something, for example a piece of music or good food, you like it because you recognize its good qualities.

create [kriéit] v. 창작하다, 창조하다
To create something means to cause it to happen or exist.

‡ seed [siːd] n. 씨, 종자; v. 씨를 뿌리다

A seed is the small, hard part of a plant from which a new plant grows.

‡ desire [dizáiər] n. 욕구, 욕망; v. 몹시 바라다, 요구하다

A desire is a strong wish to do or have something.

cross [krɔːs] v. 교차시키다; 가로지르다; a. 교차한, 가로지른; n. 십자가

If you cross your arms, legs, or fingers, you put one of them on top of the other.

‡ certainly [sə́ːrtnli] ad. 확실히, 분명히, 틀림없이

You use certainly to emphasize what you are saying when you are making a statement.

‡ fine [fain] a. 훌륭한; 질 높은, 좋은; 괜찮은, 만족할 만한

A fine person is someone you consider good, moral, and worth admiring.

＊ expert [ékspəːrt] n. 전문가; a. 숙련된, 노련한

An expert is a person who is very skilled at doing something or who knows a lot about a particular subject.

＊ delight [diláit] v. 즐겁게 하다, 매우 기쁘게 하다; n. 기쁨, 즐거움
(delighted a. 즐거워하는)

If something delights you, it gives you a lot of pleasure.

hesitate [hézətèit] v. 주저하다, 머뭇거리다, 망설이다

If you hesitate, you do not speak or act for a short time, usually because you are uncertain, embarrassed, or worried about what you are going to say or do.

＊ straighten [streitn] v. 똑바르게 하다, 곧게 하다

If you straighten something, you make it tidy or put it in its proper position.

flick [flik] v. 가볍게 치다, 튀기다; (혀 등을) 갑자기[날름] 움직이다; n. 가볍게 치기

If you flick something away, or off something else, you remove it with a quick movement of your hand or finger.

lint [lint] n. 실보푸라기
Lint is small unwanted threads or fibers that collect on clothes.

consider [kənsídər] v. 고려하다, 숙고하다
If you consider something, you think about it carefully.

author [ɔ́:θər] n. 저자, 필자
The author of a piece of writing is the person who wrote it.

pale [peil] a. 창백한; 엷은, 연한; 희미한; v. 엷어지(게 하)다
If someone looks pale, their face looks a lighter color than usual, usually because they are ill, frightened, or shocked.

vision [víʒən] n. 환상; 상상력; 시력, 통찰력
A vision is the experience of seeing something that other people cannot see, for example in a religious experience or as a result of madness or taking drugs.

principal [prínsəpəl] n. 장(長), 교장; a. 주요한, 제1의
The principal of a school is the person in charge of the school.

nod [nad] v. (고개를) 끄덕이다, 끄덕여 나타내다; n. (고개를) 끄덕임
If you nod, you move your head downward and upward to show agreement, understanding, or approval.

explode [iksplóud] v. 폭발하다, 격발하다; 폭발시키다
If someone explodes, they express strong feelings suddenly and violently.

glare [glɛər] v. 노려보다; 번쩍번쩍 빛나다; n. 섬광; 노려봄
If you glare at someone, you look at them with an angry expression on your face.

clasp [klæsp] v. (꽉) 움켜쥐다; 고정시키다, 죄다; n. 악수, 포옹; 걸쇠, 버클
If you clasp someone or something, you hold them tightly in your hands or arms.

surround [səráund] v. 둘러싸다, 에워싸다; n. 둘러싸는 것; 환경, 주위
If a person or thing is surrounded by something, that thing is situated all around them.

⁑ fancy [fǽnsi] a. 화려한, 고급스러운; v. 원하다, ~하고 싶다; n. 공상, 상상
If you describe something as fancy, you mean that it is special, unusual, or elaborate, for example because it has a lot of decoration.

⁑ obvious [ábviəs] a. 명백한, 분명한 (obviously ad. 분명히, 명백하게)
If something is obvious, it is easy to see or understand.

복습 nightmare [náitmɛər] n. 악몽
A nightmare is a very frightening dream.

⁎ detective [ditéktiv] n. 탐정, 형사
A detective is someone whose job is to discover what has happened in a crime or other situation and to find the people involved.

복습 stare [stɛər] v. 응시하다, 뚫어지게 보다
If you stare at someone or something, you look at them for a long time.

복습 afraid [əfréid] a. 두려워하는, 걱정하는; ~할 용기가 없는
If you are afraid of someone or afraid to do something, you are frightened because you think that something very unpleasant is going to happen to you.

⁑ disappoint [disəpɔ́int] v. 실망시키다, 낙담시키다 (disappointed a. 실망한, 좌절된)
If things or people disappoint you, they are not as good as you had hoped, or do not do what you hoped they would do.

⁑ hang [hæŋ] v. 축 늘어지다, 매달리다; 걸다, 달아매다; 교수형에 처하다
If something hangs in a high place or position, or if you hang it there, it is attached there so it does not touch the ground.

⁑ alike [əláik] a. 비슷한, 동등한; ad. 마찬가지로, 동등하게
If two or more things are alike, they are similar in some way.

⁑ interrupt [intərʌ́pt] v. 중단하다, 가로막다, 저지하다
If you interrupt someone who is speaking, you say or do something that causes them to stop.

promising [prámisiŋ] a. 전도유망한, 기대할 수 있는
Someone or something that is promising seems likely to be very good or successful.

squabble [skwabl] n. 시시한 싸움, 언쟁, 티격태격; v. (하찮은 일로) 옥신각신하다
When people squabble, they quarrel about something that is not really important.

settle [setl] v. (논쟁 등을) 해결하다, 끝내다; 안정되다, 진정되다; 자리를 잡다
If people settle an argument or problem, or if something settles it, they solve it, for example by making a decision about who is right or about what to do.

inform [infɔ́:rm] v. 알려주다, 통지하다; 정보를[지식을] 제공하다
(informed decision n. 정보에 근거한 결정)
An informed guess or decision is one that likely to be good, because it is based on definite knowledge or information.

particular [pərtíkjələr] a. 특정한, 특별한, 특유의
You use particular to emphasize that you are talking about one thing or one kind of thing rather than other similar ones.

face [feis] v. ~을 마주보다, 향하다; 직면하다; 직시하다
If someone or something faces a particular thing, person, or direction, they are positioned opposite them or are looking in that direction.

Chapter 10

1. **What was the setting of the story Miss McWord finished telling?**

   A. A haunted restaurant

   B. A haunted hospital

   C. A haunted hotdog stand

   D. A haunted hamburger stand

2. **Who was one of the loudest fans in the audience at the reading?**

   A. Mr. Crosswire

   B. Mrs. Crosswire

   C. Muffy

   D. Arthur

3. On what condition would Mr. Crosswire disband PAWS?

A. Miss McWord let Mr. Crosswire help her read the next story.

B. Muffy had to be the main character of the next story.

C. Miss McWord had to read another story.

D. Miss McWord had to hold more events at the library.

4. What was something that Miss McWord did not do very often?

A. She did not read very often.

B. She did not smile very often.

C. She did not write very often.

D. She did not garden very often.

5. How did Arthur feel when he closed his eyes while listening to the story?

A. He felt too scared to listen any more.

B. He felt goosebumps on his skin.

C. He felt a chill creep up his spine.

D. He felt inspired to write a story.

Check Your Reading Speed

1분에 몇 단어를 읽는지 리딩 속도를 측정해보세요.

$$\frac{182 \text{ words}}{\text{reading time (} \quad \text{) sec}} \times 60 = (\quad) \text{ WPM}$$

Build Your Vocabulary

dare [dɛər] v. 감히 ～하다, 무릅쓰다, 도전하다
If you dare to do something, you do something which requires a lot of courage.

steal [sti:l] v. 훔치다, 도둑질하다
If you steal something from someone, you take it away from them without their permission and without intending to return it.

haunt [hɔ:nt] v. (유령 등이) 출몰하다, 자주 나오다; (생각 따위가) 계속 떠오르다
(haunted a. 유령이 나오는)
A ghost or spirit that haunts a place or a person regularly appears in the place, or is seen by the person and frightens them.

stand [stænd] n. 매점, 가판대; 태도; v. 서다, 일어서다; 참다, 견디다
A stand is a small shop or stall, outdoors or in a large public building.

clap [klæp] v. 박수를 치다; n. 박수 (소리)
When you clap, you hit your hands together to show appreciation or attract attention.

cheer [ʧiər] v. 환호성을 지르다, 응원하다; n. 환호(성)
When people cheer, they shout loudly to show their approval or to encourage someone who is doing something such as taking part in a game.

sigh [sai] v. 한숨 쉬다; n. 한숨, 탄식
When you sigh, you let out a deep breath, as a way of expressing feelings such as disappointment, tiredness, or pleasure.

^복^습 **after all** idiom (예상과는 달리) 결국에는; 어쨌든
After all is used to show that something is the opposite of what you first intend to do or expect to happen.

disband [disbǽnd] v. (조직을) 해산하다, 해체하다
If someone disbands a group of people, or if the group disbands, it stops operating as a single unit.

[:] **condition** [kəndíʃən] n. 조건; 상태, 상황
When you agree to do something on condition that something else happens, you mean that you will only do it if this other thing also happens.

^복^습 **crack** [kræk] v. 금이 가다, 깨다; n. 갈라진 금; 갑작스런 날카로운 소리
If something hard cracks, or if you crack it, it becomes slightly damaged, with lines appearing on its surface.

[*] **village** [vílidʒ] n. 마을, 촌락
A village consists of a group of houses, together with other buildings such as a church and a school, in a country area.

[*] **forest** [fɔ́:rist] n. 숲, 산림
A forest is a large area where trees grow close together.

^복^습 **familiar** [fəmíljər] a. 친숙한, 잘 알고 있는; 친한; 잘 알려진
If someone or something is familiar to you, you recognize them or know them well.

[*] **chill** [tʃil] n. 냉기, 한기, 오싹한 느낌; v. 아주 춥게 만들다
(send a chill up one's spine idiom 등골을 오싹하게 하다)
If something sends a chill through you, it gives you a sudden feeling of fear or anxiety.

[*] **creep** [kri:p] v. (crept–crept) 살금살금 걷다, 기다; n. 포복
If something creeps somewhere, it moves very slowly.

spine [spain] n. 등뼈, 척추
Your spine is the row of bones down your back.

1장

page 5

"나 배고파요." D.W.가 말했습니다.

그녀는 부엌에 앉아, 아침식사를 기다리고 있었습니다.

"참을성을 가지렴, 얘야." 엄마가 말했습니다. "아빠는 거의 다 준비됐단다."

D.W.는 손가락을 테이블 위에 두드렸습니다. 그녀는 참는 것을 좋아하지 않았습니다. 그것은 너무 오래 걸렸습니다. 그리고 참는 것보다 더 싫은 유일한 것은 참을성을 가지라는 말을 듣는 것이었습니다.

"조금만 더." 리드 씨가 말했습니다. 그는 가스레인지 앞에서 바빴습니다. "연하게 구운 다음... 가루 설탕을 조금..."

page 6

"맛있겠다." D.W.가 말했습니다. 그녀는 입술을 핥았습니다.

"냠냠." 아기 케이트가 높은 아기용 의자에 앉아 말했습니다. 그녀도 입술을 핥았습니다.

"너무 오래 걸리게 하는 말아요, 여보." 리드 부인이 말했습니다. "아이들은 다 준비됐어요."

리드 씨는 접시를 들어 테이블로 가지고 왔습니다. "짜잔!" 그가 외쳤습니다. "특별 주문한, 세계적으로 유명한 우피 와플입니다! 대통령, 운동선수, 록스타들이 가장 좋아하는 음식! 한 입마다 통밀의 영양이 담겨 있습니다!"

"우피!" D.W.가 말했습니다.

"이제 접시만 주면, 내가 기꺼이 음식을 떠줄—"

아서가 뛰어 들어왔습니다.

"좋은 아침이에요, 엄마, 아빠... 저 가야 해요. 앗!"

page 8

아서는 예상치 못하게 아빠와 충돌하면서, 와플을 공중으로 쳤습니다.

D.W.가 헉 소리를 냈습니다.

아서가 가리켰습니다.

하지만 리드 씨가 행동을 개시했습니다. 그는 떨어지는 와플을 접시 위로 받으며 잡은 후, 그것을 테이블 위에 놓았습니다.

D.W.가 박수를 쳤습니다. "나의 영웅!" 그녀가 말했습니다.

아빠는 인사했습니다. "내가 그 여름을 캣스킬에서 웨이터를 하며 보낸 게 다행이지."

"더 해봐요." 아기 케이트가 말했습니다.

리드 씨는 미소 지었습니다. "아니야, 얘야. 내 행운을 시험하지는 말자꾸나."

"죄송해요." 아서가 말했습니다. "제가 어디로 가는지 보고 있지 않았던 것 같아요."

"그런 것 같구나." 엄마가 동의했습니다. "그런데 너 왜 그렇게 서두르니?"

아서는 먹으려고 앉았습니다. "저 도서관에 가야 하거든요." 그는 와플의 반쪽을 입 안에 채워 넣었습니다.

page 9

"조금 천천히 먹으렴." 엄마가 말했습니다. "주스도 좀 마시고. 목 메이고 싶진 않잖니? 도서관에 뭐가 있기에 와플 먹는 걸 못 기다리니?"

"'혼비백산 클럽'의 새 책이 오늘 들어와요. 전 첫 번째로 줄을 서고 싶어요."

리드 부인은 감명을 받았습니다. "네가 도서관에 간다고? 토요일에? 네 자유 의지로?"

"와!" 아빠가 말했습니다. "뭐라고 토달기 힘들겠는데. 그런데 조금 과장하는 것 아니니? 그 책들이 그렇게 빨리 날아가 버리듯 대출된다고?"

"거의 그렇다니까요." 아서가 말했습니다. "그 책들은 정말 인기 있어요. 저는 지난번에 나온 책을 3주 동안 기다렸어요."

"왜 사람들이 그 책을 그렇게 좋아하는 것 같니?" 엄마가 물었습니다.

page 10

아서는 확신하지 못했습니다. "아마도 그게 좀 무서우면서도 재미있는 게 동시에 있어서 그런 것 같아요."

"드문 조합이지." 리드 씨가 말했습니다.

"맞아요." 아서가 말했습니다. 그는 다른 한 입을 삼키고 문을 향해 달려갔습니다.

그리고 그는 떠났습니다.

"뭐가 그렇게 중요한 건지 모르겠네요." D.W.가 말했습니다. "그래도 아서 오빠가 도서관에 간다는 건 좋네요."

"어째서 그렇지?" 엄마가 물었습니다.

D.W.는 접시를 바라보았습니다. "왜냐하면." 그녀가 말했습니다. "저한테 더 많은 와플이 남는 거잖아요."

2장

page 11

아서는 서둘러 길을 따라 갔습니다. 그는 그가 곧 읽게 될 새 책을 생각했습니다. 그는 이번에는 얼마나 무서울지 궁금했습니다. 지난달의 '어느 마녀가 진짜?'편은 세 장 만에 벌벌 그를 떨게 했습니다.

아서는 빗물 배수구 위로 높이 뛰었습니다. 그는 지하세계의 어떤 생물체가 그 구멍에서 올라와 그를 잡는 것을 원하지 않았습니다. 그것은 '콘스토커의 밤'편에서 수지에게 큰 대가를 치르게 했던 종류의 부주의함이었습니다.

page 12

아서는 모퉁이를 돌아 앞에 있는 도서관을 보았습니다.

"오, 안 돼!"

건물 밖에는 아이들의 긴 줄이 이미 형성되어 있었습니다. 줄은 뱀처럼 계단 아래로 구불구불 내려와 도보로 이어져 있었습니다.

"안녕, 아서!"

"여기야!"

줄의 끝에서 프랜신, 버스터, 수 엘렌, 그리고 브레인이 그에게 손을 흔들고 있었습니다.

아서는 합류하기 위해 터덜터덜 걸어갔습니다. 줄은 너무 길었습니다! 믿을 수가 없었습니다.

"우리 좀 더 일찍 만났어야 했나봐." 프랜신이 말했습니다.

"맞아." 브레인이 말했습니다. "해 뜨기 전이라던가 말이야."

"이봐!" 버스터가 말했습니다. "성급하게 단정 짓지 말자. 누가 알아? 어쩌면 다들 여기에 공부하러 온 것일 수도 있잖아."

"토요일에?" 프랜신이 말했습니다.

page 13

수 엘렌이 하품했습니다. "그것도 토요일 이른 아침에?" 그녀가 덧붙였습니다.

아서는 한숨 쉬었습니다. "나는 그렇게 생각하지 않아, 버스터. 게다가, 내가

방금 지나온 모든 애들이 '혼비백산 클럽' 셔츠나 모자를 쓰고 있었어."

"우리가 안에 들어간다고 해도." 프랜신이 말했습니다. "우리가 빌릴 수 있는 새 책은 남아 있지 않을 거야."

"우리 그냥 예전 책을 빌려서 다시 읽어야 할 것 같아." 아서가 말했습니다.

버스터가 끄덕였습니다. "맞아, '미라 숨결의 저주'편은 어때? 이 책을 읽으면 이빨 닦지 않겠다고 말할 수 없을걸..."

"아니면 '옷장 속의 해골'편." 브레인이 말했습니다. "난 그 책 읽고 나서 일주일 동안 같은 옷을 입었어."

구름이 머리 위로 몰리고, 태양이 사라졌습니다.

"가장 무서운 것을 잊지 마." 프랜신이 말했습니다. "'좀비 교생 선생님'편."

page 14

"오오!" 모두가 같이 말했습니다.

그들은 모두 몸서리쳤습니다.

"나는 왜 저 TV 트럭이 여기 있는 건지 궁금해." 버스터가 말했습니다. 그는 길 건너를 가리켰습니다.

"아마 기자들도 팬인가 봐." 수 엘렌이 말했습니다.

"아니면." 브레인이 말했습니다. "토요일 아침에 도서관 밖에 선 줄을 보는 것이 뉴스일지도."

"그건 신경 쓰지 마." 프랜신이 말했습니다. "봐! 문이 열리고 있어."

모두들 고개를 돌려 봤습니다. 도서관 문이 끼익 소리를 내며 천천히 열렸습니다. 불길한 그림자가 안에서 나타나, 천천히 앞으로 움직였습니다. 그림자가 계단에 닿자 태양이 다시 나타났습니다.

"좋은 아침입니다." 도서관 사서인 터너 부인이 말했습니다. "엄청난 수의 사람들이군요."

아이들이 환호했습니다.

page 16

그녀는 조용히 하라는 의미로 군중에게 손을 들었습니다.

"모두를 이렇게 보게 되어서 영광입니다. 그러나 나쁜 소식이 있어요. 오늘 '혼비백산 클럽'의 새 책을 빌리러 오신 분들은 대출하실 수가 없습니다. 사실, 그 시리즈의 모든 책을 추후 공지가 있을 때까지 우리 서가에서 치워둘 것입니다."

아이들은 깜짝 놀랐습니다. 그들은 믿을 수 없다는 탄식을 내뱉었습니다.

"난 한 시간 동안 기다렸어요!"

"불공평해요!"

"무슨 일이에요?"

터너 부인은 손가락을 입술에 댔습니다. "그게 제가 지금 말할 수 있는 전부입니다. 당연히 여러분은 들어오셔서 다른 책을 빌려 가셔도 됩니다. 하지만 조용히요. 기억하세요, 여기는 도서관

입니다."

그녀는 안으로 다시 들어갔습니다.

문이 그녀 뒤로 닫혔지만, 아무도 다시 열려고 서두르지 않았습니다.

3장

page 17

"이해할 수가 없어." 아이들이 걸어 나가자 아서가 말했습니다. "누가 우리 책들을 없애고 싶어 하는 거지?"

"우리 책 전부가 아니라." 프랜신이 그를 상기시켰습니다. "단지 '혼비백산 클럽' 책만."

"왜 그걸 괴롭히는 거지?" 버스터가 물었습니다.

누구도 재빨리 말할 수 있는 답을 가지고 있지 않았습니다.

"이봐!" 수 엘렌이 말했습니다. "저걸 봐!"

그녀는 길 건너에 있는 TV 가게를 가리켰습니다. '혼비백산 클럽'의 로고가 화면을 채우고 있었습니다.

모두들 무슨 일이 일어나고 있는지 보기 위해 길을 건넜습니다.

page 18

"엘우드시의 교외에서." 뉴스 기자가 말했습니다. "학부모 단체가 몇권의 아동용 책을 공립 도서관 서가에서 몰아

냈습니다."

사진은 도서관과 줄을 지어 기다리고 있는 아이들을 보여 주었습니다.

"저거 우리잖아." 브레인이 말했습니다.

"어떻게 우리가 TV에 이렇게 빨리 나올 수 있지?" 버스터가 말했습니다.

"내가 생각하기에." 브레인이 말했습니다. "저 사람들이 인공위성을 써서 저 사진들을 스튜디오로 전송한 것 같아."

"쉿!" 프랜신이 말했습니다. "나는 나머지를 듣고 싶어."

"PAWS라고 불리는 학부모 단체—이상한 이야기를 반대하는 부모들의 모임—는 무서운 이야기가 아이들에게 악영향을 끼친다고 말합니다. 저희는 저자 E. A. D'Poe의 의견을 위해 연락을 시도했지만 연결에 성공하지 못했습니다. 더 많은 지지를 얻기 위해, PAWS는 염려하는 학부모들을 위한 '집회를 연다고 합니다. 그들은 내일 오후 1시에 도서관 계단에서 만난다고 합니다."

page 20

뉴스는 다른 이야기로 넘어갔습니다.

"적색경보!" 버스터가 소리쳤습니다. "만약 우리가 다시 혼비백산 놀라고 싶다면, 우리 뭔가를 해야 해—그것도 빨리."

"하지만 뭘?" 프랜신이 물었습니다.

브레인은 머리를 긁었습니다. "일반적

으로 말해서." 그가 말했습니다. "미성년자는 법적 대응책이나 중재에 제한적으로만 접근할 수 있어."

"그게 무슨 말이냐면." 아서가 말했습니다. "우리가 할 수 있는 것이 얼마 없다는 것이지." 그는 친구들을 둘러보았습니다. "하지만 난 아직 포기하고 싶지 않아. 우리 전에 포기한 적이 없잖아!"

"물론 우리 포기했었지." 버스터가 말했습니다.

"아주 많이." 프랜신이 말했습니다.

"우리 포기하는 거 잘하잖아." 수 엘렌이 말했습니다.

page 21

"중요할 때에는 그렇지 않아." 아서가 말했습니다. "너희가 차고 청소하는 것을 도와줘서, 내가 '갤럭시 어벤져스'를 보러 갈 수 있었던 것 기억해?"

아서는 그 일을 아주 잘 기억하고 있었습니다.

프랜신은 쓰레기가 든 무거운 봉투 두 개를 옮기고 있었습니다. 브레인은 페인트 통을 쌓고 있었고, 아서는 목재를 벽에 기대어 줄 세우고 있었습니다.

버스터는 바닥을 쓸고 있었습니다. 그가 끝냈을 때, 그는 빗자루를 코 위에 올려 균형을 잡기 시작했습니다. 갑자기 빗자루가 떨어지면서, 목재들을 넘어뜨렸습니다. 그것들은 페인트 캔 위로 떨어졌고, 페인트 캔이 열려서 온 주위에 페인트를 쏟았습니다.

프랜신은 너무 놀라 쓰레기봉투를 놓쳤고, 쓰레기가 모두 굴러 떨어져 나왔습니다.

"나 그때 기억해." 프랜신이 말했습니다. "참 잘 한 짓이었어, 버스터!"

"그건 사고였어!" 버스터가 말했습니다. "누구한테나 일어날 수 있는 일이었어."

page 22

"요점은," 아서가 말했습니다. "우리가 영화를 보러갈 수 있었다는 거야."

"다음 날에 말이지." 브레인이 말했습니다. "모든 것을 다 청소하고 말이야."

"맞아." 아서가 말했습니다. "그러니까 우리가 가는 길에 장애물이 좀 있긴 했어. 그럼 버스터가 수학 때문에 도움이 필요했던 때는 언제?"

버스터는 소파에 앉아 매우 집중하고 있었습니다. 그의 숙제와 수학책이 그의 주위에 널려 있었습니다. "자, 버스터." 아서가 말했습니다. "넌 알 수 있어."

그와 프랜신의 가슴에는 7과 3이 적혀 있었습니다. 팔은 그들 가운데에서 곱셈 표시 x를 몸에 드리우고 서 있었습니다. 브레인은 이마에 = 표시를 붙이고 있었습니다.

"빨리 생각해." 브레인이 말했습니다. "내 이마가 간질거리기 시작했어."

"21!" 버스터가 말했습니다. "답은 21이야. 나 여전히 기억하고 있어."

page 23

"봤지?" 아서가 말했습니다.

"난 버스터에게 곱셈을 가르쳤던 것을 잊고 있었어." 프랜신이 말했습니다. "우리가 그걸 할 수 있다면, 이것도 할 수 있을 거야."

"맞아." 버스터가 말했습니다. "우리 데모하자! 우리 책을 되찾을 때까지 더 이상 숙제는 없는 거야."

아서는 한숨 쉬었습니다.

브레인은 팔짱을 끼었습니다.

프랜신은 어이가 없어 눈을 굴렸습니다.

"알겠어, 알겠어." 버스터가 말했습니다. "시도할 가치는 있었잖아. 하지만 누구 더 좋은 생각 있어?"

아무도 없었습니다. 어쨌든 아직까지는요.

4장

page 24

점심식사 후 아서, 버스터, 프랜신, 브레인, 그리고 수 엘렌은 슈가 볼에서 만났습니다.

"우리가 해야 하는 일은," 브레인이 말했습니다. "우리만이 이런 의견을 가지고 있는 것이 아니라는 것을 양적으로 보여 주는 일이야."

"뭐라구?" 버스터가 말했습니다.

"브레인이 하는 말은," 프랜신이 말했습니다. "우리가 PAWS에 많은 아이들이 책이 돌아오길 바란다는 것을 보여 주어야 한다는 거야."

"머피는 어디 있는지 모르겠네." 프랜신이 말했습니다. "내가 전화해서 우리랑 같이 하자고 메시지를 남겼는데."

"우리는 그녀를 기다려줄 수 없어." 버스터가 말했습니다. "우리는 움직이고, 움직이고, 또 움직여야 해! 우리 조치를 취해야 해!"

page 25

"나 아이디어가 하나 있어." 프랜신이 말했습니다. "우리 탄원서에 서명을 받자. 그게 우리 엄마가 오래된 시청 건물을 지킬 때 했던 일이야. 우리가 PAWS 사람들한테 책이 얼마나 많은 지지를 받고 있는지 보여 준다면, 아마도 우린 그들의 마음을 바꿀 수 있을 거야."

"하지만 그냥 애들의 지지만 가지고는 안 돼." 브레인이 말했습니다. "어른들의 지지도 필요해."

"우리가 충분한 시간을 가지고 있을까?" 수 엘렌이 말했습니다. "PAWS 집회는 내일이야."

"글쎄." 아서가 말했습니다. "알아보는 데는 한 가지 방법밖에 없지."

아이들은 몇 개의 무리로 나눠져 마을 전체로 흩어졌습니다. 버스터와 아서는 팀을 이뤄 아서네 집 앞 잔디밭으로 갔습니다.

"좋은 아침입니다, 엘우드시의 여러분!" 버스터가 확성기에 대고 소리쳤습니다.

차 두 대가 멈추지 않고 붕 하고 지나갔습니다.

page 26

"지금 밖으로 나오세요!" 버스터가 계속했습니다. "어메이징 아서가 경이로운 재주를 펼칩니다! 그리고 나서 우리의 책을 구하기 위해 이름을 서명해 주세요."

아서는 잠수경과 수영복을 입고 있었습니다. 그는 공기를 넣은 물놀이 풀장 위에 있는 밧줄에서 균형을 잡으려고 하고 있었습니다.

"버스터, 너 이거에 대해서 확신해?" 아서가 물었습니다. 그는 별로 어메이징한 기분이 아니었습니다. 그는 그가 어메이징하게 보인다고 생각하지도 않았습니다.

"광고랑 마찬가지야." 버스터가 속삭였습니다. "사람들이 서명하기 전에, 우리가 그들의 관심을 끌어야 해. 이제, 시작해!"

아서는 숨을 들이 쉬고 빗자루로 균형을 잡으며 밧줄 위를 걷기 시작했습니다.

지나가던 아이들 몇 명이 멈춰서 구경했습니다.

"침착해, 거기!"

"와! 뒤로! 뒤로!"

아서는 한쪽으로 기울었다가, 다시 다른 쪽으로 기울었습니다. 빗자루가 프로펠러처럼 돌아가면서, 그는 물속으로 떨어졌습니다.

page 28

아이들은 웃음을 터트렸습니다. "한 번 더! 한 번 더!" 그들은 소리쳤습니다.

"어메이징 아서는 기꺼이 다시 재주를 펼칠 것입니다." 버스터가 말했습니다. "하지만 먼저 우리 후원자들의 한마디가 있겠습니다."

그는 탄원서를 꺼내 자신들이 무엇을 하려고 하는지 설명했습니다.

아서가 수건으로 물기를 말리는 동안, 아이들은 그들의 이름을 서명했습니다.

한편, 프랜신과 수 엘렌은 공원에서 줄넘기 놀이를 했습니다. 줄을 선 아이들이 뛸 차례를 기다리고 있었습니다.

프랜신이 노래 불렀습니다.

"PAWS가 우리의 책을 빼앗아 갔네,
그래서 난 오늘 도움을 청하고 있네.
지금 줄을 서서 이름을 서명하세요.
그게 나의 줄넘기 놀이의 요점이네."

page 29

각각의 아이들은 줄넘기를 마치고, 탄원서에 서명했습니다.

"다음!" 프랜신이 말했습니다.

한편, 버스 정류장에서는, 브레인이 버스를 기다리는 승객들을 교육시키려고 하고 있었습니다. 그는 칠판을 흐름도와 방정식 그리고 책들의 이름으로 채워 둔 상태였습니다.

"보시는 대로," 그가 군중들에게 말했습니다. "우리는 학교생활에 끼치는 영향이 기하학적이라고 예상합니다. 학습 곡선에서의 뚜렷한 상승을 주목하세요."

그는 포인터로 가리켰습니다.

버스 승객들은 고개를 저었습니다. 몇몇은 그들의 귀를 가렸습니다.

"이것이 우리의 가설입니다." 브레인은 계속했습니다. "오락적인 독서가 많은 교육적인 혜택을 가져올 것이라는 것이요. 따라서 우리는 여러분에게 탄원서에 서명할 것을 요청합니다."

"우리 서명할게." 누군가가 말했습니다. "네가 더 이상 설명하지 않겠다고 약속하면 말이지."

page 30

"그래, 제발!"

"아무렴 그렇고말고."

"우린 동의해."

그들은 브레인의 클립보드 주위로 몰려들었습니다.

그는 미소 지었습니다. 만약 다른 아이들도 그가 하는 것과 같은 성공을 거두고 있다면, 결국엔 그들에게 기회가 있을지도 모릅니다.

5장

page 31

아서와 버스터는 그들이 이웃에서 받을 수 있는 서명을 다 모으고 나서, 더 많은 서명을 받기 위해 공원으로 갔습니다.

"어메이징 아서를 여기서 하고 싶지 않은 게 확실해?" 버스터가 물었습니다.

아서는 확신했습니다. 그는 이미 하루 분량만큼 충분히 어메이징했었습니다.

"우리 나눠지자." 그가 말했습니다. "그렇게 하는 것이 우리가 더 많은 지역을 맡을 수 있어."

버스터는 연못 주위의 앉는 자리로 향하는 동안, 아서는 들판 너머로 갔습니다.

page 32

처음에 아서는 롤러 블레이드를 타거나 자전거를 타거나 그냥 게임을 하고 있는 사람들을 따라잡느라 애를 먹었습니다.

"미안해요, 우리 바빠요."

"나중에 봐요."

"지금은 안 돼요. 매치 포인트에요."

그것은 조금 실망스러웠습니다. 그는 분수 주위의 식물들을 다듬고 있는 한 부인을 보았습니다. 마침내, 움직이고 있지 않는 사람을 발견한 것입니다.

그는 다가가 자신을 소개했습니다.

"실례합니다, 부인." 그는 말했습니다. "잠시 동안 이야기할 수 있을까요?"

"이미 그러고 있잖니." 부인이 말했습니다. 그녀의 안경은 코 아랫부분에 걸쳐 있었습니다. "나한테 허락을 얻기엔 조금 늦은 것 같구나."

아서는 망설였습니다. "그게 사실인 것 같네요. 그래도 훌륭한 목적을 위해서 그랬던 것이에요. 적어도 저희들은 그렇게 생각해요."

page 34

"그럼 그 훌륭한 목적이 무엇인지, 내가 물어도 될까?"

"한 학부모 단체가 저희가 좋아하는 책을 도서관에서 없앴어요." 아서가 설명했습니다. "저희는 그 책을 다시 돌려 놓으려고 하고 있어요. 하지만 저희는 많은 사람들이 저희와 같이 느낀다는 것을 보여 주고 싶어요. 그래서 저희는 이 청원을 시작했어요. 저희를 위해서 서명해 주실 수 있으세요?"

부인은 잠시 머뭇거렸습니다. "오늘 자원봉사를 하는 게 나뿐만이 아닌가 보구나." 그녀는 아서를 오래 쳐다보았습니다. "내가 서명할지 안 할지는 모두 책에 달려 있어. 난 네 부모님의 바람을 거스르고 싶지 않구나."

"오, 그렇지 않을 거예요. 제 부모님은 제가 다양한 것을 읽는 걸 좋아하세요. 저희 아빠는 그게 식품군이랑 같대요. 모든 걸 조금씩 먹는 것이 건강에 좋잖아요."

"좋은 조언이구나." 그 부인이 말했습니다.

"게다가," 아서가 말했습니다. "이 책들은 저희가 가장 좋아하는 것들이에요. '혼비백산 클럽' 책들이요."

page 35

부인은 무릎을 꿇어앉고는 안경을 코위로 밀어서 고쳐 썼습니다.

"정말? 그 '혼비백산 클럽' 책 말이야? 네가 그 책을 읽는단 말이니… 음…?"

"아서요." 그는 그녀와 악수했습니다. "제가 읽느냐고요? 물론이죠! 전 한 권도 빼먹지 않았어요."

부인은 얼굴을 찌푸렸습니다. "그렇다면 상황이 심각하구나. 아마도 내가 직접 학부모 단체랑 이야기를 해봐야겠다!"

그녀는 일어나서 그녀의 원예 도구들을 모았습니다.

"포기하지 마렴, 아서. 너와 네 친구들은 좋은 일을 하는 거야."

아서는 어리둥절해 보였습니다. "물론이죠. 감사합니다—그럴게요…"

그는 그녀가 떠나는 것을 바라보았습니다. 그리고 그는 클립보드를 내려다보았습니다. "이봐요! 기다리세요! 서명하는 것을 잊으셨어요."

하지만 그녀는 가버렸습니다.

6장

page 36

그날 오후, 아서, 프랜신, 수 엘렌, 그리고 버스터는 아이스크림콘을 먹으며 슈가 볼을 나왔습니다.

"서명을 모으는 것은 힘든 일이야." 버스터가 말했습니다.

"우리가 이름을 충분히 모았다고 생각해?" 프랜신이 물었습니다.

아서는 콘 주위에서 떨어지는 아이스크림을 핥았습니다. "그런 것 같아. 이렇게 많은 페이지가 있잖아. PAWS가 우리 얘기를 들어주면 좋겠어."

프랜신은 손목시계를 보았습니다. "브레인은 어디 있는 건지 모르겠네. 다섯 시에 우리랑 만나기로 했는데."

page 37

"저길 봐!" 버스터가 말했습니다. "머피가 온다."

"근데 쟨 대체 어디에 있었던 거지?"

프랜신이 말했습니다. "우리 오늘 쟤의 도움을 받을 수 있었을 텐데."

머피는 큰 미소를 짓고 있었습니다. "좋은 소식이야, 애들아!" 그녀가 발표했습니다. "우리 부모님이 내일 원더월드에서 큰 파티를 연대." 그녀는 잠시 멈췄습니다. "그리고 내가 초대하고 싶은 사람은 누구나 초대할 수 있대."

"와!" 아서가 말했습니다. 원더월드는 주위에 있는 최고의 축제이자 테마파크였습니다. 그곳에 공짜로 간다는 것은 정말 대단한 대접이었습니다.

"그거 멋진데." 수 엘렌이 말했습니다.

"나도 넣어줘!" 프랜신이 말했습니다.

프랜신은 머피가 그녀의 콘을 보고 있다는 것을 알아챘습니다.

"한 입 먹을래?" 그녀가 물었습니다. 그녀는 콘을 내밀었습니다.

머피는 뒤로 물러섰습니다. "음, 아니 괜찮아. 우리 엄마가 허락하지 않을 거야—너무 많은 지방과 설탕이라고." 그녀는 눈을 감았습니다. "그거 좀 치워줘, 제발!"

page 38

그때 브레인이 모퉁이에 나타났습니다. 그는 한 손에 신문을 쥐고 있었습니다.

"미안 내가 늦었지, 애들아. 내가 하는 얘기를 들을 때까지 기다—" 그는 갑자기 멈췄습니다. "오... 안녕, 머피."

머피는 인도를 쳐다보았습니다.

"네가 뭘 알아냈는데?" 프랜신이 물었습니다.

브레인은 머피의 방향을 힐끗 쳐다보았습니다. "들어 봐." 그가 말했습니다. "오늘 신문에 책이 금지된 거랑 그 배후에 있는 사람의 인터뷰에 대한 전체 기사가 나왔어. 중요한 부분으로 넘어갈게."

그는 신문을 읽기 시작했습니다.

"'아이들은 이 책들이 끼치는 해악을 몰라요.' 밀리센트 크로스와이어 씨가 말했다. '불쌍한 내 딸 머피는 한 권만 읽고도 끔찍한 악몽을 꾼답니다.'"

모두들 머피를 쳐다보았습니다. 그녀는 여전히 인도에 난 금을 살피고 있었습니다.

page 40

브레인은 좀 더 읽었습니다. "'우리는 다른 아이들을 구하기 위해 *PAWS*를 시작했어요.' 밀리센트 씨의 남편 에드 씨가 덧붙였다. '우리는 걱정하는 부모님들을 위한 집회를 내일 도서관에서 열거예요. 그 이후에, 우리의 모든 후원자들은—나이가 많고 적음에 상관없이—원더월드에서 열리는 축하 행사에 참가할 수 있어요.'"

버스터는 충격을 받았습니다. "머피, 너네 부모님이 PAWS를 시작하셨니?"

머피는 올려다보았습니다. "응." 그녀가 말했습니다.

"그렇지만 왜?" 프랜신이 물었습니다.

머피는 입술을 깨물었습니다.

"나 그것 좀 보게 해줘." 아서가 브레인에게 말했습니다.

브레인은 그에게 신문을 주었습니다.

아서는 인터뷰를 전부 다 읽었습니다. "이건 그냥 아무런 원더월드 파티가 아니잖아." 그가 말했습니다. "안 그래, 머피? 이건 PAWS를 지지하는 사람들만을 위한 거야."

머피가 어깨를 으쓱했습니다. "뭐, 네가 그렇게 엄밀하게 말하고 싶다면..."

page 41

"오, 안 돼!" 버스터가 말했습니다.

"우리는 우리 책들을 되찾아야 해, 머피." 아서가 말했습니다. "이해하지 못하겠니?"

머피는 망설였습니다. 그리고 그녀는 숨을 깊이 들이쉬고 팔짱을 꼈습니다.

"넌 단지 무엇이 너에게 더 많은 것을 의미하는지 결정해야 해." 그녀가 말했습니다. "원더월드—아니면 멍청한 책들. 선택은 너한테 달렸어."

7장

page 42

"뭐가 그렇게 복잡하다는 건지 모르겠네." D.W.가 말했습니다. 그녀는 양손을 저울질하는 것처럼 내밀었습니다. "무서운 책 몇 권이 여기 있고, 공짜로 가는 원더월드가 여기 있어." 그녀는 원더월드를 나타내는 손이 더 무거운 것을 들고 있는 것처럼 무릎까지 내렸습니다. 다른 쪽 손이 솟구쳐 올라갔습니다. "경쟁이 안 돼."

그녀와 아서는 거실에 앉아 있었습니다. 아서는 그녀에게 머피와 머피의 부모님과 있었던 문제에 대해 말했습니다.

"그렇게 간단하지 않아." 아서가 말했습니다.

D.W.가 웃었습니다. "나한테는 그래. 오빠 원더월드가 얼마나 멋진지 알잖아. 거기에는 최고의 롤러코스터가 있어. 사람들이 토하고 난리도 아니야. 넌 어떻게 생각하니, 케이트?"

page 43

그들의 아기 여동생이 아기용 놀이 울타리 안에서 바라보고 있었습니다. 그녀의 손이 올라갔다 내려갔습니다.

"봤지, 오빠?" D.W.가 말했습니다. "심지어 케이트도 뭐가 올바른 일인지 알고 있어. 단지 아기인데도 말이야."

"뭘 하는데 올바른 일을 말하는 거니?" 리드 부인이 일을 하다 잠시 휴식을 취하며 물었습니다.

"아서 오빠가 공짜로 원더월드에 가게 됐어요." D.W.가 말했습니다.

"정말?" 리드 부인이 말했습니다. "어

떻게 그런 일이 생겼니?"

아서가 엄마에게 말했습니다.

"그렇구나." 엄마가 말했습니다. "음, 아서, 원더월드에 가는 사람치고는, 넌 그다지 행복해 보이지 않는구나."

아서는 한숨 쉬었습니다. "제가 D.W.에게 말하려고 한 것처럼, 이건 그렇게 간단하지 않아요. 저는 머피의 파티를 놓치고 싶지 않아요. 하지만 저는 제가 제일 좋아하는 책을 잃고 싶지도 않아요. 그리고 제가 PAWS를 지지하지 않는다면 가는 것도 옳지 않은 일 같아요."

page 44

리드 부인은 고개를 끄덕였습니다. "매우 어려운 상황이구나, 아서. 이건 마치 대차대조표 같아. 더하기가 있고 빼기가 있지. 네가 모든 것을 다 더하고 나면, 넌 네가 옳다고 생각하는 일을 해야만 해. 심지어 그게 희생해야 한다는 걸 의미한다고 해도 말이야."

아서는 더 생각하기 위해 밖을 돌아다녔습니다. 자신이 믿는 것을 지지하는 것이 왜 이렇게 어려워야 할까요?

"난 다른 사람들이 어떻게 생각하는지 알고 싶어." 아서가 중얼거렸습니다.

"내가 어떻게 생각하는지에 대해 말해줄게." 아빠가 차고에서 말했습니다. "내 인생은 활짝 열린 책처럼 단순해. 그건, 요리책이지." 리드 씨는 크게 벌인

음식 출장 서비스 사업으로 매우 바빴습니다. 하지만 지금은, 그는 상자들을 살펴보고 있었습니다.

page 45

"저는 어려운 질문들에 대한 답을 찾을 수 있는 책이 있으면 좋겠어요." 아서가 말했습니다.

그는 상황을 아빠에게 설명했습니다.

"그런 책이 있으면 참 좋겠구나." 아빠도 동의했습니다. "아마도 베스트셀러가 될 거야." 아빠는 상자를 열었습니다. "아, 내가 찾던 것이 여기 있구나."

그는 광대 의상을 꺼냈습니다. "오늘 오후에 아동 병원 자선 행사에 필요한 것이지."

그는 의상을 입기 시작했습니다.

"만약에 저 혼자만 PAWS에 항의하기로 결정한 사람이면 어쩌죠?" 아서가 말했습니다. "만약 내 모든 친구들이 그것 대신에 원더월드로 가기로 결정하면 어떻게 해요?"

리드 씨는 대머리 가발을 고쳐 썼습니다. "네가 믿는 무언가를 위해 바보같아 보이는 것을 두려워할 수는 없지. 그 고무로 된 코 좀 나한테 주겠니."

아서가 그걸 아빠에게 건넸습니다. 그리고 그는 생각하려고 앉았습니다.

page 47

뿌웅!

아서가 뛰어 올랐습니다.

"오, 고맙다." 아빠가 말했습니다. "방귀 쿠션이 어디 있는지 궁금했었거든." 리드 씨는 그것을 주머니에 넣었습니다.

그는 손목시계를 보았습니다.

"난 이제 가야겠구나. 한가지만 기억하렴, 아서. 난 네가 친구들이 하는 것을 하고 싶어 한다는 걸 알아. 하지만 나를 보렴."

아서는 광대 의상을 입은 아빠를 바라보았습니다.

"가끔씩 광대들은 팀으로 일한단다." 아빠는 주위에 있는 가상의 광대들과 악수를 했습니다. "그리고 가끔씩 그들은 자신들만의 힘으로 스포트라이트를 감내하며 서 있단다." 그는 살짝 몸을 숙여 인사했습니다.

아서는 한숨을 쉬었습니다. 그리고 가끔씩 광대들은 슬퍼 보였습니다. 그가 지금 느끼는 것과 같이요.

8장

page 48

다음 날 아침 도서관에서, 크로스와이어 부부는 계단 맨 꼭대기에 서 있었습니다. 머피는 부모님 뒤로 계속 몸을 숨겼지만, 그들은 계속 그녀를 앞으로 끄집어냈습니다.

아이들과 부모님의 무리가 그들 주위에 모여 있었습니다.

크로스와이어 씨는 휴대용 마이크에 대고 말했습니다. "모두들 와 주셔서 감사합니다. 저는, 파크가와 레이크우드가의 모퉁이에 있고, 거의 매일 밤 10시까지 열려 있는 크로스와이어 모터스의 에드 크로스와이어입니다. 하지만 저는 이걸 제 자신을 위해서 하고 있는 것이 아닙니다. 저는 우리의 아이들을 구하기 위해서 하고 있습니다!"

page 49

그의 말은 환호성과 정중한 박수를 받았습니다.

떨어진 한쪽에서, 아서는 엄마와 함께 서 있었습니다. 그는 '우리 책에서 PAWS(손을) 떼!'라고 적힌 피켓을 들고 있었습니다.

아무도 주의를 기울이는 것 같지 않았습니다.

"아무도 보이지 않아요." 아서가 말했습니다. "아무래도 원더월드가 이겼나 봐요."

"그렇게 확신하지 마렴." 리드 부인이 말했습니다. "아직 시간이 있어."

"여기 작은 우리 딸이 있습니다." 에드 크로스와이어 씨가 계속 했습니다. 그는 머피의 손을 들었습니다. "저희는 PAWS를 우리 딸 때문에 시작했습니다. 하지만 저희는 여러분 모두도 역시 신경 쓰고 있습니다."

바로 그때 버스터, 프랜신, 브레인, 그리고 수 엘렌이 모퉁이를 돌아 나타났습니다. 그들은 손에 피켓을 가지고 들고 있었습니다.

'법(LAW)을 지켜라, PAWS가 아니라!'

'PAWS를 끝내라!'

"너희들 여기 있구나!" 아서가 말했습니다. "나 이상하게 생각하던 차였어."

page 50

"미안 우리가 늦었지." 브레인이 말했습니다. "우리 서명을 더 받아 왔어."

그는 탄원서 종이를 내밀었습니다. 거기에는 이제 수십 수백 개의 이름이 있었습니다.

"그럼 누가 이것들을 크로스와이어 씨에게 줄래?" 버스터가 물었습니다.

"네가 해." 브레인이 말했습니다.

"나 말고." 버스터가 말했습니다. "네가 해."

"누구?" 수 엘렌이 말했습니다.

"너 말고." 프랜신이 말했습니다. "아서는 어때?"

"좋아!"

"좋은 생각이야."

"음, 아서..." 브레인이 말했습니다.

아서는 깊은 숨을 들이켰습니다. "좋아." 그가 말했습니다. "내가 할게!"

그는 탄원서를 팔 아래에 끼고 군중들 사이로 헤쳐 나갔습니다.

관람차도 없고, 아이스크림도 없고, 롤러코스터도 없습니다.

page 51

"실례합니다. 실례합니다. 지나갈게요."

솜사탕도 없고, 범퍼카도 없고, 유령의 집도 없습니다.

계단의 가장 위에서, 아서는 크로스와이어 씨 앞에서 멈췄습니다. 그는 원더월드의 그런 모든 멋진 것들을 놓치게 되어서 아쉬울 것입니다. 하지만 이것이 더 중요했습니다.

"만약 우리가 태도를 취하지 않는다면, 우리의 믿음은 실패할 것입니다. 우리는 반드시—"

"실례합니다, 크로스와이어 씨, 제발요." 아서가 말했습니다. "우리 얘기 좀 해요."

"지금은 안 된다, 아서야. 지금 순조롭게 진행되고 있어."

"바로 그거예요, 크로스와이어 씨. 지금 바로 저희의 권리를 넘어서고 계시잖아요. 그건 공평하지 않아요. 아이들을 위해서 말하자면, 우리는 정말 우리 책들을 돌려받고 싶어요. 우린 여기 지지하는 사람들의 서명을 모아 왔—"

page 53

"그거 멋지구나, 아서. 네 태도에 대해서는 정말 감탄한단다. 하지만 나를 믿으렴, 이것이 바로 너 자신을 위한 일이야!

이 책들은 그야말로 엄청난 문제라고."

"그 책들을 읽어봤나요?" 군중 속에서 한 목소리가 물었습니다.

아서는 몸을 돌렸습니다. 그 목소리는 친숙했습니다.

놀랍게도, 그것은 에드 크로스와이어 씨에게도 친숙했습니다. 그는 군중들을 내다보았습니다. 그는 약간 혼란스러워 보였습니다.

아서는 다음에 무슨 일이 일어날지 궁금했습니다.

9장

page 54
"거기 누구죠?" 에드 크로스와이어 씨가 물었습니다.

나머지 군중들은 조용해졌습니다.

"질문에 대답해요." 목소리가 말했습니다. "당신은 당신이 비난하는 책을 읽어본 적이 있나요?"

군중들은 말하는 사람을 드러내기 위해 뒤로 물러났습니다. 아서는 그녀를 알아보았습니다. 그녀는 공원에서 그가 말을 걸었던 부인이었습니다.

크로스와이어 씨는 헛기침을 했습니다. "저는 당신이 돈을 준대도 이 책들을 읽지 않을 것이라고 자랑스럽게 얘기할 수 있습니다!"

그 부인은 한숨을 쉬었습니다. "놀랍지도 않구나." 그녀가 말했습니다.

page 54
크로스와이어 씨는 깜짝 놀란 것처럼 보였습니다. "이런, 나 당신을 알아요... 맥워드 선생님이시죠, 제 초등학교 영어 선생님이요."

"그래, 나란다, 에드워드." 그녀는 계단을 올랐습니다. "네 기억력이 아직 남아 있어서 기쁘구나. 네 상식도 그렇다면 좋을 텐데."

"맥워드 선생님, 저는 선생님께 제가 예전에 가졌던 것만큼의 상식을 지금도 전적으로 가지고 있다고 확실히 말씀드릴 수 있어요."

그녀는 그의 옆에 섰습니다. "그게 사실일지도 모르지." 그녀가 인정했습니다. "네가 전혀 변하지 않았다는 것이 보이는구나. 넌 절대 책 읽는 아이가 아니었지. 넌 아이들이 읽고 싶어 하는 이야기를 만들기 위해 작가들이 얼마나 노력하는지 인식할 수 있니? 각각의 이야기는 씨앗과 같단다, 에드워드. 한 아이가 한 이야기를 읽으면, 그 씨앗은 다른 이야기를 읽고 싶다는 욕망으로 자라날 거야. 그것이 모든 작가들이 바라는 일이지."

크로스와이어 씨는 팔짱을 끼었습니다. "오, 정말이요? 맥워드 선생님, 선생님은 확실히 훌륭한 선생님이셨어요.

하지만 어떻게 작가들이 바라고 있는 것에 대해서 그렇게 잘 알고 있는 전문가처럼 말씀하실 수 있죠?"

page 57

"뭐, 나는 스스로가 작가이기도 하니까."

"오. 우리 모두 그 얘기를 듣게 되어 기쁘네요." 크로스와이어 씨는 망설이며 말했습니다. "우리가 알 만한 책이 있나요?"

맥워드 선생님은 크로스와이어 씨의 재킷을 똑바로 하고 그의 어깨에서 보푸라기를 떼었습니다. "네가 읽었던 것은 아니란다, 에드워드. 네 상식이나 기타 등등을 고려해 보면 말이다. 하지만 네가 물었으니까 하는 말인데, 내가 '혼비백산 클럽' 책의 저자란다."

"선생님이!" 크로스와이어 씨가 창백해지면서 말했습니다. 그는 맥워드 선생님이 자신을 교장실로 데려가는 갑작스러운 환상을 보았습니다.

"부인이요?" 아서가 말했습니다.

"저 사람이?" 프랜신, 버스터, 수 엘렌, 그리고 브레인이 함께 말했습니다.

부인은 고개를 끄덕였습니다. "E. A. D'Poe는 내 필명이야."

page 58

머피는 흥분에 거의 폭발할 지경이었습니다. "D'Poe 선생님!" 그녀는 울부짖었습니다. "제가 선생님의 제일가는 팬이에요! 저는 선생님 책을 전부 다 가지고 있어요. 제가 선생님의 사인을 좀 받을 수—" 그녀의 부모님이 그녀를 노려보았습니다. "아차!"

그녀는 부모님이 주위를 에워싸자 손으로 입을 막았습니다.

"너 전부 다 읽었다고?" 그녀의 아빠가 말했습니다.

"그리고 도대체 언제 그랬니?" 그녀의 엄마가 물었습니다. "메리 앨리스 크로스와이어, 너 꽤 멋진 설명을 가지고 있겠구나."

"오 이런!" 머피가 말했습니다.

"네가 이 책들을 다 읽었다면." 크로스와이어 부인이 말했습니다. "그럼 명백하게도 너에게 악몽을 꾸게 한 것은 이 책들 중에 하나가 아니겠구나. 그럼 그게 뭐였던 거지?"

"음, 글쎄요..." 머피는 그의 엄마가 탐정처럼 얘기할 때가 싫었습니다.

"잠깐만, 여기." 크로스와이어 씨가 말했습니다. "이제야 누가 내 한센-페퍼 아이스크림 한 통을 다 먹었는지 알겠구나."

page 59

"그리고 그렇게 했다고 시인하기가 무서웠겠지." 그녀의 엄마가 말했습니다. "메리 앨리스, 너 그렇게 먹는 것이 너한테 악몽을 꾸게 한다는 것을 알잖아."

"우리 너에게 매우 실망했단다." 그녀

의 아빠가 말했습니다.

"그리고 당신한테도 매우 실망했어요." 머피의 엄마가 그녀의 남편에게 말했습니다. "도대체 아이스크림을 한 통이나 가지고 뭘 하고 있던 거예요?"

"음, 나는..."

아서는 거의 미소 지었습니다. 머피와 그녀의 아빠는 모두 고개를 푹 숙이고 서 있었습니다. 그들은 매우 닮아 보였습니다.

맥워드 선생님이 목을 가다듬었습니다. "전도유망한 가족이 옥신각신 하는데 끼어들고 싶지는 않지만, 우린 여전히 정리해야 할 문제가 있군요. 에드워드, 네가 내가 쓴 이야기 중 하나를 충분히 길게 듣는다면 아마도 너의 실언을 수습할 수 있을 거야. 그러면 너는 누가 이 책을 읽어야 하는지에 대해서 잘 알고 결정할 수 있을 테지."

page 60

"오, 그럼요. 멋진 생각이에요."

바로 그 순간에는, 무슨 일이든지 그의 부인을 마주보고 있는 것보다는 나았습니다.

10장

page 61

"그리고 그날 이후로, 그 누구도 다시는 저주받은 햄버거 가판대에서 감히 물건을 훔치지 못했습니다."

맥워드 선생님은 책을 내려놓았습니다.

군중들은 박수 치고 환호했습니다. 그중 가장 시끄러운 팬은 에드 크로스와이어 씨였습니다.

"어때요, 아빠?" 머피가 물었습니다.

그는 한숨 쉬었습니다. "아무래도 나는 그 전체 이야기를 알지도 못한 채, 너 같은 아이들이 책을 읽는 것을 막지 말았어야 했던 것 같구나."

"아마도." 맥워드 선생님이 말했습니다. "너도 결국에는 변하긴 한 것 같구나, 에드워드."

page 63

"그래서 우리 책을 돌려받을 수 있나요, 크로스와이어 씨?" 아서가 물었습니다.

"난 PAWS를 한 가지 조건하에 해산하겠어." 크로스와이어 씨가 말했습니다.

모두들 조용해졌습니다.

"그럼 그 조건이 뭐에요?" 머피가 말했습니다.

"맥워드 선생님이 우리에게 다른 이야기를 읽어준다는 조건으로." 크로스와이어 씨는 그녀를 보았습니다. "제발요?"

"좋아!"

"다른 이야기!"

"좋았어!"

맥워드 선생님은 미소를 지었습니다. 그건 그녀가 평소에는 자주 하지 않는 것이었습니다. 그녀는 다른 책을 소리 내며 펼쳤습니다.

"마을 사람들은 왜 그 노인이 혼자서 깊고 어두운 산 속에서 사는지 아무도 몰랐습니다. 오로지 숲속의 동물들만 이 그의 비밀을 알았죠..."

아서는 뒤로 편안히 앉아서 눈을 감고 익숙한 오싹함이 등골을 서늘하게 하는 것을 느꼈습니다.

Chapter 1

1. B D. W. drummed her fingers on the table. She didn't like to be patient. It took too long. And the only thing worse than being patient was being told to be patient.

2. C Mr. Read picked up the platter and brought it toward the table. "Ta-dah!" he announced. "By special request, my World-Famous Whoopee Waffles. The favorite of presidents, professional athletes, and rock stars. There's whole-grain goodness in every bite."

3. D But Mr. Read sprang into action. He caught the falling waffles on the platter, then dished them onto the table.

4. C "The new Scare-Your-Pants-Off Club book will be there today. I want to be first in line."

5. A "But I think it's great that Arthur is going to the library." "Why is that?" asked her mother. D.W. eyed the platter. "Because," she said, "it leaves more waffles for me!"

Chapter 2

1. C Arthur hurried down the street. He was thinking about the new book he would soon be reading. He wondered how he would get the pants scared off him this time.

2. D Arthur jumped high over a storm grate. He didn't want some creature from the Underworld rising through the holes to grab him.

3. B Arthur turned the corner and saw the library ahead of him. "Oh, no!" Outside the building, a long line of kids had already formed. It snaked down the stairs and along the sidewalk.

4. A "I wonder why that TV truck is here," said Buster. He pointed across the street. "Maybe the reporters are fans, too," said Sue Ellen.

5. D "It's a pleasure to see you all. However, I have some bad news. Anyone who has come to check out the new Scare-Your-Pants-Off Club book today will be unable to do so. In fact, all of the books in that series have been removed

from our shelves until further notice."

Chapter 3

1. A *"In suburban Elwood City,"* said the news reporter, *"a parents group has chased some children's books off the shelves of the public library."* The picture showed the library and all the kids waiting in line.

2. D *"The parents group, called PAWS—Parents Against Weird Stories—says the scary stories are bad for kids. We tried unsuccessfully to reach E. A. D'Poe, the author of the books, for comment. . . ."*

3. C "But I'm not willing to give up yet. We've never given up before!" "Sure we have," said Buster. "Lots of times," said Francine. "We're good at giving up," said Sue Ellen.

4. B " Remember the time you helped clean out my garage so I could go with you to see *Galaxy Avengers?*"

5. A *He and Francine were wearing the numbers 7 and 3 on their chests. Pal was standing between them with an x, the multiplication symbol, draped over him. The Brain had an equal sign taped to his forehead.*

Chapter 4

1. C Just after lunch Arthur, Buster, Francine, the Brain, and Sue Ellen met at the Sugar Bowl.

2. A "I have one idea," said Francine. "We could get signatures on a petition. That's what my mom did to save the old City Hall building. If we can show the PAWS people how much support the books have, maybe we can change their minds."

3. B "Step right up!" Buster went on. "See the Amazing Arthur perform feats of wonder! Then sign your name to save our books." Arthur was wearing a diving mask and bathing suit. He was trying to balance on a rope above an inflatable wading pool.

4. C Meanwhile, Francine and Sue Ellen were jumping double Dutch in the park. A line of kids was waiting for a turn to jump.

5. D "We'll sign," said someone, "if you promise to stop explaining things to us."

Chapter 5

1. D After Arthur and Buster had collected all the signatures they could in the neighborhood, they went to the park to gather more.

2. C "Are you sure you don't want to be the Amazing Arthur here, too?" Buster asked. Arthur was sure. He had been amazing enough for one day. "Let's split up," he said. "That way we can cover more ground."

3. D He did spot an old woman tending some plants near a fountain. Finally, someone who wasn't on the move.

4. A "Oh, you wouldn't be. My parents like me to read different things. My father says it's like the food groups. It's healthy to have a little bit of everything."

5. B He watched her leave. Then he looked down at his clipboard. "Hey! Wait! You forgot to sign." But the woman was gone.

Chapter 6

1. C "Do you think we have enough names?" asked Francine. Arthur licked the drips around his cone. "I think so. There are pages and pages. I just hope PAWS will listen to us."

2. A Muffy was wearing a big smile. "Great news, everyone!" she announced. "My parents are having a big party tomorrow at WonderWorld." She paused. "And I can invite anyone I want."

3. D At that moment the Brain came around the corner. He was clutching a newspaper in one hand. "Sorry I'm late, everyone. Wait till you hear what I just—" He stopped suddenly. "Oh . . . hello, Muffy." Muffy looked at the sidewalk.

4. B   Buster was shocked. "Muffy, your mom and dad started PAWS?" Muffy looked up. "Yes," she said.

5. C   "You just have to decide which means more to you," she said. "WonderWorld—or a bunch of silly books. The choice is yours."

Chapter 7

1. C   "I don't know what's so complicated," said D.W. She put out her hands as though she were balancing things in a scale. "Some creepy books here. Free WonderWorld here." She lowered her WonderWorld hand to her knees, as though it was holding something heavy. The other hand shot up. "No contest."

2. A   Mrs. Read nodded. "It's a difficult situation, Arthur. It's like a balance sheet. There are pluses and minuses. When you add everything up, you have to do what you think is right—even if it means making a sacrifice."

3. C   He pulled out a clown costume. "Just what I need for this afternoon's children's hospital benefit."

4. C   Mr. Read adjusted his bald wig. "Can't be afraid to look foolish for something you believe in. Give me that rubber nose, please."

5. D   "Sometimes clowns work as a team." His father shook hands with a bunch of imaginary clowns around him. "And sometimes they stand under the spotlight all by themselves." He made a little bow.

Chapter 8

1. B   At the library the next morning, the Crosswires stood at the top of the steps. Muffy kept ducking behind her parents, but they kept pulling her out in front of them.

2. D   Mr. Crosswire spoke into a portable microphone. "Thank you all for coming. I'm Ed Crosswire of Crosswire Motors, corner of Park and Lakewood, open most nights till ten. But I'm not doing this for me. I'm doing it to save our kids!"

3. C   "You're here!" said Arthur. "I was beginning to wonder." "Sorry we're

late," said the Brain. "We stopped for more signatures."

4. A "Not you," said Francine. "How about Arthur?" "Yeah!" "Good idea." "Well, Arthur . . . ," said the Brain. Arthur took a deep breath. "All right," he said. "I'll do it!" Holding the petitions under one arm, he worked his way through the crowd.

5. B "Have you read them?" asked a voice from the crowd. Arthur turned around. That voice was familiar.

Chapter 9

1. A Mr. Crosswire looked startled. "Why, I know you . . . . You're Miss McWord, my grade-school English teacher."

2. B She stood beside him. "That may be true," she admitted. "I see you haven't changed. You never were much of a reader. Can you appreciate how hard a writer works to create stories kids will like to read? Each story is like a seed, Edward. If a child reads one, the seed may grow into the desire to read another. That's something every writer hopes for."

3. D "Nothing you've read, Edward, considering your common sense and all. But since you've asked, I'm the author of the Scare-Your-Pants-Off Club books."

4. C "Just a minute, here," said Mr. Crosswire. He stared at Muffy. "Now I know who ate my quart of Haasen-Pfeffer ice cream." "And then was afraid to admit it," said her mother. "Mary Alice, you know eating like that gives you bad dreams."

5. A "Oh. Yes. Excellent idea." At this particular moment, anything was better than facing his wife.

Chapter 10

1. D "And since that night, nobody has dared to steal anything from the haunted hamburger stand again."

2. A The crowd clapped and cheered. Among the loudest fans was Ed Crosswire.

3. C "I will disband PAWS on one condition," said Mr. Crosswire. Everyone fell silent. "And that condition is?" said Muffy. "That Miss McWord will read us another story." Mr. Crosswire looked at her. "Please?"

4. B Miss McWord smiled, something she didn't do very often. She cracked open another book.

5. C Arthur sat back and closed his eyes as a familiar chill crept up his spine.

아서와 혼비백산 클럽
(Arthur and the Scare-Your-Pants-Off Club)

1판 1쇄 2013년 7월 8일
1판 10쇄 2020년 4월 29일

지은이 Marc Brown
기획 이수영
책임편집 김보경 차소향
콘텐츠제작및감수 롱테일북스 편집부
저작권 김보경
마케팅 김보미 정경훈

펴낸이 이수영
펴낸곳 (주)롱테일북스
출판등록 제2015-000191호
주소 04043 서울특별시 마포구 양화로 12길 16-9(서교동) 북앤빌딩 3층
전자메일 helper@longtailbooks.co.kr
(학원·학교에서 본도서를 교재로 사용하길 원하시는 경우 전자메일로 문의주시면
자세한 안내를 받으실 수 있습니다.)

ISBN 978-89-5605-674-6 14740

롱테일북스는 (주)북하우스 퍼블리셔스의 계열사입니다.

이 도서의 국립중앙도서관 출판시도서목록(CIP)은 서지정보유통지원시스템 홈페이지(http://seoji.nl.go.kr)와
국가자료공동목록시스템(http://www.nl.go.kr/kolisnet)에서 이용하실 수 있습니다. (CIP 제어번호 : CIP 2013009574)

Arthur and the Scare-Your-Pants-off Club

ISBN 978-89-5605-674-6 14740

Longtail Books

For Tolon

Chapter 1

"I'm hungry," said D.W.

She was sitting in the kitchen, waiting for **breakfast**.

"Be **patient**, sweetie," said her mother. "Your father's almost ready."

D.W. **drum**med her fingers on the table. She didn't like to be patient. It took too long. And the only thing worse than being patient was being *told* to be patient.

"Just another moment," said Mr. Read. He was busy at the **stove**. "Lightly **brown**ed . . . a little **powder**ed sugar . . ."

"**Yum**mm," said D.W. She **lick**ed her lips.

"Yummm, yummm," said baby Kate in her **high chair**. She licked her lips, too.

"Don't take too long, dear," said Mrs. Read. "The kids are **rev**ving up."

Mr. Read picked up the **platter** and brought it toward the table. "Ta-dah!*" he **announce**d. "By special **request**, my World-Famous Whoopee Waffles. The favorite of **president**s, **professional athlete**s, and rock stars. There's whole-**grain goodness** in every **bite**."

"Whoopee!*" said D.W.

"Now, if I could just have your plates, I'll be happy to **serve**—"

Arthur **rush**ed in.

"Morning, Mom, Dad . . . Gotta* run. Oops!*"

★ **ta-dah** 나오신다, 기대하시라. 무엇인가를 처음 소개할 때 말하는 감탄사.

✳ **whoopee** 와, 야. 기쁨을 나타낼 때 쓰는 감탄사.

✳ **gotta** 'have to', 'must'의 구어체.

✳ **oops** 이런, 아이쿠. 실수를 하거나 놀랐을 때 쓰는 감탄사.

Arthur **unexpected**ly **collide**d with his father, **knock**ing the waffles high into the air.

D.W. **gasp**ed.

Arthur pointed.

But Mr. Read **sprang into action**. He caught the falling waffles on the platter, then **dish**ed them onto the table.

D.W. **clap**ped. "My hero!" she said.

Her father took a **bow**. "Lucky I **spent** that summer **wait**ing **on** tables in the Catskills."

"More," said baby Kate.

Mr. Read smiled. "I don't think so, honey. Let's not **push my luck**."

"Sorry," said Arthur. "I guess I wasn't looking where I was going."

"I guess not," his mother **agree**d. "But why are you in such a hurry?"

Arthur sat down to eat. "I have to get to the library." He **stuff**ed half of a waffle into his mouth.

"Slow down a little," said his mother. "Drink some juice. You don't want to **choke**. What's at the library that can't wait for waffles?"

"The new Scare-Your-Pants-Off★ Club book will be there today. I want to be first in line."

Mrs. Read was **impress**ed. "You're going to the library? On a Saturday? Of your own **free will**?"

"Wow!" said his father. "Hard to **argue** with that. But aren't you **exaggerating** a little? Are these books really flying off the **shelves**?"

"**Just about**," said Arthur. "They're really **popular**. I waited three weeks for the last one."

"Why do you think everyone likes them so much?" asked his mother.

★ **Scare-Your-Pants-Off** '너무 놀라 바지가 벗겨질 정도이다'는 표현으로, 본 책에서는 '혼비백산'으로 번역했다.

9

Arthur wasn't sure. "Maybe it's because they're **sort of scary** and fun at the same time."

"An **unusual combination**," said Mr. Read.

"Right," said Arthur. He **swallow**ed another bite and **dash**ed for the door.

Then he was gone.

"I don't see what the **big deal** is," said D.W. "But I think it's great that Arthur is going to the library."

"Why is that?" asked her mother.

D.W. **eye**d the platter. "Because," she said, "it leaves more waffles for me!"

Chapter

2

Arthur hurried down the street. He was thinking about the new book he would soon be reading. He **wonder**ed how he would get the pants scared off him this time. Last month's *Which **Witch** Is Which?* had started him **shiver**ing by the third page.

Arthur jumped high over a storm **grate**. He didn't want some **creature** from the Underworld rising through the holes to **grab** him. It was just that **sort of careless**ness that had **cost** Susie so **dearly** in *Night of the Cornstalker.*

Arthur turned the corner and saw the library ahead of him.

"Oh, no!"

Outside the building, a long line of kids had already **form**ed. It **snake**d down the stairs and along the **sidewalk**.

"Hi, Arthur!"

"Over here!"

At the end of the line, Francine, Buster, Sue Ellen, and the Brain were **waving** to him.

Arthur **trudge**d over to join them. The line was so long! It was **unbelievable**.

"Guess we should have met earlier," said Francine.

"Yeah," said the Brain. "Like just before **dawn**."

"Hey!" said Buster. "Let's not **jump to conclusions**. Who knows? Maybe they're just all here to study."

"On a Saturday?" said Francine.

Sue Ellen **yawn**ed. "Early on a Saturday?" she added.

Arthur **sigh**ed. "I don't think so, Buster. Besides, everyone I just passed is wearing a SYPOC★ shirt or hat."

"Even once we get in," said Francine, "there won't be any new books left."

"I guess we could **check out** some of the old ones to read again," said Arthur.

Buster **nod**ded. "Yeah. How about *Curse of the Mummy's Breath?* Talk about not **brush**ing your teeth . . ."

"Or *Skeletons in the Closet*," said the Brain. "I wore the same clothes for a week after I read that one."

The clouds **roll**ed overhead, and the sun disappeared.

"Don't forget the scariest one of all," said

★ **SYPOC** 'Scare-Your-Pants-Off'의 첫글자를 딴 약자.

Francine. "*Zombie **Substitute** Teacher.*"

"Oooooh!" everyone said together.

They all **shudder**ed.

"I wonder why that TV truck is here," said Buster. He pointed across the street.

"Maybe the reporters are fans, too," said Sue Ellen.

"Or maybe," said the Brain, "it's news to see a line outside a library on a Saturday morning."

"**Never mind** that," said Francine. "Look! The doors are opening."

They all turned to watch. The library doors **creak**ed open slowly. A **sinister shadow** appeared within, slowly moving forward. The sun came back out as the shadow reached the steps.

"Good morning," said Ms. Turner, the **librarian**. "This is quite a **turnout**."

The kids **cheer**ed.

She held up a hand to quiet the **crowd**.

"It's a pleasure to see you all. However, I have some bad news. Anyone who has come to check out the new Scare-Your-Pants-Off Club book today will be unable to do so. In fact, all of the books in that series have been **removed** from our **shelves** until **further notice**."

The kids were **stun**ned. They **let out** a **shriek** of **disbelief**.

"I've been waiting for an hour!"

"No **fair**!"

"What happened?"

Ms. Turner held a finger to her lips. "That's all I can say at this time. **Naturally** you're all welcome to come in and pick out something else. But quietly. Remember, this is a library."

She went back inside.

The doors closed behind her—and nobody **rush**ed to open them again.

Chapter
3

"I don't **get it**," said Arthur as the kids walked away. "Who would want to **get rid of** our books?"

"Not all our books," Francine **remind**ed him. "Just the Scare-Your-Pants-Off Club books."

"Why **pick on** them?" asked Buster.

Nobody had a quick answer.

"Hey!" said Sue Ellen. "Look at that!"

She pointed to a TV store across the street. The SYPOC logo filled the screen.

Everyone **cross**ed the street to find out

what was going on.

"In suburban Elwood City," said the news reporter, *"a parents group has chased some children's books off the shelves of the public library."*

The picture showed the library and all the kids waiting in line.

"That's us," said the Brain.

"How did we get on TV so fast?" asked Buster.

"I imagine," said the Brain, "that they used a **satellite** downfeed★ to get these pictures back to the studio."

"Shhh!" said Francine. "I want to hear the rest."

"The parents group, called PAWS—Parents Against Weird Stories—says the scary stories are bad for kids. We tried unsuccessfully to

---

★ **satellite downfeed** 인공위성(satellite)을 이용해 텔레비전 방송 신호(feed)를 전송하는 기술.

*reach E. A. D'Poe, the **author** of the books, for* *comment. Hoping to build more **support**, PAWS is holding a **rally** for **concerned** parents. They will meet on the library steps at one o'clock tomorrow afternoon."*

The news moved on to other stories.

"Red **alert**!" Buster **shout**ed. "If we ever want the pants scared off us again, we've got to do something—and fast."

"But what?" asked Francine.

The Brain **scratch**ed his head. "**Generally** speaking," he said, "**minor**s have **limit**ed **access** to **legal recourse** or **arbitration**."

"Which means," said Arthur, "that there isn't much we can do." He looked around at his friends. "But I**'m** not **willing to give up** yet. We've never given up before!"

"Sure we have," said Buster.

"Lots of times," said Francine.

"We're good at giving up," said Sue Ellen.

"Not when it's important," said Arthur. "Remember the time you helped clean out my **garage** so I could go with you to see *Galaxy Avengers?*"

Arthur remembered it well.

*Francine was carrying two heavy bags of **trash**. The Brain was **stack**ing paint cans, and Arthur was lining up two-by-fours★ against the wall.*

*Buster was **sweep**ing the floor. When he finished, he started **balancing** the **broom** on his nose. Suddenly the broom fell off, **knock**ing over the two-by-fours. They fell onto the paint cans, which opened and **spill**ed paint everywhere.*

*Francine was so **startled** that she **drop**ped the trash bags, and all the **garbage tumble**d out.*

"I remember that," said Francine. "Nice going, Buster!"

"It was an **accident**!" said Buster. "It could

★ **two-by-four** 2×4인치 크기의 목재.

21

have happened to anyone."

"The point is," said Arthur, "we **made it** to the movie."

"The *next* day," said the Brain. "After we cleaned up everything."

"Okay," said Arthur, "so we hit a few **bump**s along the way. What about the time Buster needed help with his **math**?"

*Buster was sitting on his **couch**, deep in **concentration**. His homework and math books were **spread** out around him. "Come on, Buster," said Arthur. "You can get this."*

*He and Francine were wearing the numbers 7 and 3 on their **chest**s. Pal was standing between them with an x, the **multiplication symbol**, **drape**d over him. The Brain had an **equal** sign taped to his **forehead**.*

*"Think quickly," said the Brain. "My forehead is beginning to **itch**."*

"Twenty-one!" said Buster. "The answer

was twenty-one. I still remember it."

"See?" said Arthur.

"I'd forgotten about teaching Buster to multiply," said Francine. "If we can do that, maybe we can do this, too."

"I know," said Buster. "Let's go on **strike**! No more homework till we get our books back."

Arthur **sigh**ed

The Brain **fold**ed his arms.

Francine **roll**ed **her eyes**.

"All right, all right," said Buster. "It was **worth** a try. But who has a better idea?"

Nobody did—not yet, anyway.

Chapter
4

Just after lunch Arthur, Buster, Francine, the Brain, and Sue Ellen met at the Sugar Bowl.

"What we need to do," said the Brain, "is **quantitative**ly **demonstrate** that we're not alone in our **opinion**."

"Huh?" said Buster.

"He means," said Francine, "we have to show PAWS that a lot of kids want their books back."

"I **wonder** where Muffy is," said Francine. "I called and left a message for her to join us."

"We can't wait for her," said Buster. "We

have to move, move, move! We have to **take action**!"

"I have one idea," said Francine. "We could get **signature**s on a **petition**. That's what my mom did to save the old City Hall building. If we can show the PAWS people how much **support** the books have, maybe we can change their minds."

"But it can't just be kids' support," said the Brain. "We'll need adults, too."

"Do we have enough time?" said Sue Ellen. "The PAWS **rally** is tomorrow."

"Well," said Arthur, "there's only one way to find out."

The kids **split** into several groups and **spread** out through town. Buster and Arthur **team**ed **up** on Arthur's front **lawn**.

"Gooooood morning, Elwood City!" Buster **shout**ed into a **megaphone**.

Two cars **whiz**zed by without stopping.

"**Step** right **up**!" Buster went on. "See the **Amazing** Arthur **perform feat**s of wonder! Then sign your name to save our books."

Arthur was wearing a **diving** mask and **bathing suit**. He was trying to **balance** on a rope above an **inflatable wading** pool.

"Buster, are you sure about this?" Arthur asked. He didn't feel very amazing. He didn't think he looked amazing, either.

"It's like a **commercial**," Buster **whisper**ed. "Before we can get them to sign, we have to get their **attention**. Now, **go ahead**!"

Arthur took a **breath** and started along the rope, balancing himself with a **broom**.

A few kids passing by stopped to watch.

"Easy, there!"

"Whoa! Back! Back!"

Arthur **lean**ed one way, then the other. As the broom **twirl**ed like a **propeller**, he fell into the water.

The kids laughed. "Again! Again!" they shouted.

"The Amazing Arthur will be happy to perform again," said Buster. "But first a word from our **sponsor**."

He pulled out the petition and explained what they were trying to do.

While Arthur dried off with a towel, the kids signed their names.

Meanwhile, Francine and Sue Ellen were jumping double Dutch★ in the park. A line of kids was waiting for a turn to jump.

Francine was **chant**ing,

"PAWS has taken our books away,
So I'm asking for your help today.
Line up now and sign your name.
That's the point of my rope game."

★ double Dutch 두 개의 줄을 번갈아가면서 돌리는 줄넘기 놀이.

As each kid finished, he or she signed the petition.

"Next!" said Francine.

Over at the bus stop, the Brain was trying to **educate** the waiting **passenger**s. He had covered a **blackboard** with **flow chart**s, **equation**s, and names of books.

"As you can see," he told the crowd, "we **predict** that the **impact** on school performance will be **geometric**. **Note** the **marked** rise in the learning **curve**."

He pointed with his pointer.

The bus passengers shook their heads. A few covered their ears.

"It is our **hypothesis**," the Brain went on, "that **recreation**al reading **yield**s many **educational benefit**s. Therefore, we **invite** you to sign our petition."

"We'll sign," said someone, "if you promise to stop explaining things to us."

"Yes, please!"

"**By all means**."

"We **agree**."

They **crowd**ed around the Brain's **clipboard**.

He smiled. If everyone else was having the same success he was, they might have a chance **after all**.

Chapter 5

After Arthur and Buster had **collect**ed all the **signature**s they could in the **neighborhood**, they went to the park to **gather** more.

"Are you sure you don't want to be the **Amazing** Arthur here, too?" Buster asked.

Arthur was sure. He had been amazing enough for one day.

"Let's **split** up," he said. "That way we can cover more ground."

Buster headed for the seating area around the **pond** while Arthur **set out** across the fields.

At first Arthur had trouble **catch**ing **up with** people who were Rollerblading or biking or just playing games.

"Sorry, we're busy."

"Catch me later."

"Not now. We're at match point.*"

It was a little **discouraging**. He did **spot** an old woman **tend**ing some **plant**s near a **fountain**. Finally, someone who **was**n't **on the move**.

He walked over to **introduce** himself.

"Excuse me, ma'am," he said. "Could I speak to you for a moment?"

"You already are," said the woman. Her glasses were **perch**ed low on her nose. "It's a little late to ask my **permission**."

Arthur **hesitate**d. "I guess that's true. It's for a good **cause**, though. At least we think it is."

★ **match point** 매치 포인트. 운동 경기에서 승패를 좌우하는 마지막 1점.

"And what is this good cause, may I ask?"

"A parents group has had our favorite books **remove**d from the library," Arthur explained. "We're trying to get them back. But we want to show that a lot of people feel the same way we do. So we've started up this **petition**. Would you sign it for us?"

The woman **pause**d. "I see I'm not the only one doing **volunteer** work today." She gave Arthur a long look. "It all **depend**s on the books. I wouldn't want to **go against** your parents' wishes."

"Oh, you wouldn't be. My parents like me to read different things. My father says it's like the food groups.★ It's **healthy** to have a little **bit** of everything."

"Good **advice**," said the woman.

"Besides," said Arthur, "these books are our

★**food group** 식품군. 영양 성분이 유사한 식품들을 몇 가지로 나누어 분류한 것.

favorites: the Scare-Your-Pants-Off Club books."

The old woman sat back on her **heel**s and pushed her glasses back up on her nose.

"Really? The Scare-Your-Pants-Off Club books? Do you read them . . . um . . . ?"

"Arthur." He shook her hand. "Do I read them? Of course! I haven't **miss**ed a **single** one."

The woman **frown**ed. "Then the situation is **serious**. Maybe I should speak to this parents group myself!"

She stood up and gathered her **garden**ing **tool**s.

"Don't **give up**, Arthur. You and your friends are doing a good thing."

Arthur looked **puzzle**d. "Sure. Thanks—I think . . ."

He watched her leave. Then he looked down at his **clipboard**. "Hey! Wait! You forgot to sign."

But the woman was gone.

Chapter 6

Later that afternoon, Arthur, Francine, Sue Ellen, and Buster walked out of the Sugar Bowl, eating ice cream cones.

"**Collect**ing **signature**s is hard work," said Buster.

"Do you think we have enough names?" asked Francine.

Arthur **lick**ed the **drip**s around his cone. "I think so. There are pages and pages. I just hope PAWS will listen to us."

Francine looked at her watch. "I **wonder** where the Brain is. He **was supposed to** meet us at five."

"Look!" said Buster. "Here comes Muffy."

"Where has she been, anyway?" said Francine. "We could have used her help today."

Muffy was wearing a big smile. "Great news, everyone!" she **announce**d. "My parents are having a big party tomorrow at WonderWorld." She **pause**d. "And I can **invite** anyone I want."

"Wow!" said Arthur. WonderWorld was the best **carnival** and **theme** park around. Going there for free would be a real **treat**.

"That's **terrific**," said Sue Ellen.

"**Count** me in!" said Francine.

Francine **notice**d Muffy **eye**ing her cone.

"Want a lick?" she asked. She **held out** the cone.

Muffy backed away. "Um, no thanks. My mom won't let me—too much **fat** and sugar."

She shut her eyes. "Take it away. Please!"

At that moment the Brain came around the corner. He was **clutch**ing a newspaper in one hand.

"Sorry I'm late, everyone. Wait till you hear what I just—" He stopped suddenly. "Oh . . . hello, Muffy."

Muffy looked at the **sidewalk**.

"What did you find out?" Francine asked.

The Brain **glance**d in Muffy's **direction**. "Listen to this," he said. "There's a whole **article** in today's paper about the book **ban** and an **interview** with the people behind it. I'll **skip** to the important part."

He started reading from the newspaper.

*"'Kids don't know the **harm** these books do,' said Millicent Crosswire. 'My poor daughter, Muffy, read just one, and it gave her **awful** nightmares.'"*

Everyone looked at Muffy. She continued

to study the **crack**s in the sidewalk.

The Brain read some more. *"'We started PAWS to save other kids,' added Millicent's husband, Ed. 'We're having a big **rally** for **concern**ed parents at the library tomorrow. **Afterward**, all our **support**ers—young and old— can join us for a **celebration** at WonderWorld.'"*

Buster was **shock**ed. "Muffy, your mom and dad started PAWS?"

Muffy looked up. "Yes," she said.

"But why?" asked Francine.

Muffy **bit** her lip.

"Let me see that," Arthur said to the Brain.

The Brain gave him the newspaper.

Arthur read through the interview. "This isn't just **any old** WonderWorld party," he said. "Is it, Muffy? It's only for people who support PAWS."

Muffy **shrug**ged. "Well, if you want to get **technical** . . ."

"Oh, no!" said Buster.

"We have to get our books back, Muffy," said Arthur. "Don't you understand?"

Muffy **hesitate**d. Then she took a deep **breath** and **fold**ed her arms.

"You just have to decide which means more to you," she said. "WonderWorld—or a **bunch** of **silly** books. The **choice** is yours."

Chapter
7

"I don't know what's so **complicated**," said D.W. She put out her hands as though she were **balancing** things in a **scale**. "Some **creepy** books here. Free WonderWorld here." She **lower**ed her WonderWorld hand to her **knee**s, as though it was holding something heavy. The other hand **shot** up. "No **contest**."

She and Arthur were sitting in the living room. Arthur had told her about the problem with Muffy and her parents.

"It's not that simple," said Arthur.

D.W. laughed. "It is to me. You know

how great WonderWorld is. They have the best roller coaster. People **throw up and everything**. What do you think, Kate?"

Their baby sister was watching from her **playpen**. Her hands were going up and down.

"See, Arthur?" said D.W. "Even Kate knows the right thing to do. And she's just a baby."

"The right thing to do about what?" asked Mrs. Read, taking a **break** from her work.

"Arthur gets to go to WonderWorld for free," said D.W.

"Really?" said Mrs. Read. "How did that **come about**?"

Arthur told her.

"I see," said his mother. "Well, Arthur, for someone going to WonderWorld, you don't look very happy."

Arthur **sigh**ed. "As I was trying to tell D.W., it's not that simple. I don't want to **miss**

Muffy's party. But I don't want to lose my favorite books, either. And it's not really right to go if I don't **support** PAWS."

Mrs. Read **nod**ded. "It's a difficult situation, Arthur. It's like a balance **sheet**. There are pluses and minuses. When you add everything up, you have to do what you think is right—even if it means making a **sacrifice**."

Arthur **wander**ed outside to think some more. Why did **stick**ing **up for** what you believe in have to be so difficult?

"I wish I knew what everyone else was thinking," Arthur **mutter**ed.

"I'll tell you what I'm thinking," said his father from the **garage**. "My life's an open book.★ A cookbook, that is." Mr. Read was busy with a huge **catering** job. But right now, he was looking through boxes.

★**open book** '펼쳐진 책'이라는 표현은 어떤 사람의 행동이나 태도, 생각 등이 다 알려져 있어 알기 쉽다는 의미이다.

"I wish there was a book where I could look up the answers to hard questions," Arthur said.

He explained the situation to his father.

"That would be a good book to have," his father **agree**d. "Probably a bestseller." He opened a box. "Ah, here's what I was looking for."

He pulled out a **clown costume**. "Just what I need for this afternoon's children's hospital **benefit**."

He began putting the costume on.

"What if I'm the only one who decides to **protest** PAWS?" said Arthur. "What if all my friends decide to go to WonderWorld instead?"

Mr. Read **adjust**ed his **bald wig**. "Can't be **afraid** to look **foolish** for something you believe in. Give me that **rubber** nose, please."

Arthur handed it to him. Then he sat

down to think.

Bllaaattttt!

Arthur jumped up.

"Oh, thanks," said his father. "I **wonder**ed where that whoopee cushion★ was." Mr. Read put it in his pocket.

He looked at his watch.

"I've got to be going. Remember one thing, Arthur. I know you want to do what your friends are doing. But look at me."

Arthur **stare**d at his father in his clown **suit**.

"Sometimes clowns work as a team." His father shook hands with a **bunch** of **imaginary** clowns around him. "And sometimes they stand under the **spotlight all by themselves**." He made a little **bow**.

Arthur sighed. And sometimes clowns looked sad, the way he felt right now.

★ whoopee cushion 깔고 앉으면 방귀 소리가 나는 쿠션.

Chapter 8

At the library the next morning, the Crosswires stood at the top of the steps. Muffy kept **duck**ing behind her parents, but they kept pulling her out in front of them.

A **crowd** of kids and parents was **gather**ed around them.

Mr. Crosswire spoke into a **portable microphone**. "Thank you all for coming. I'm Ed Crosswire of Crosswire Motors, corner of Park and Lakewood, open most nights till ten. But I'm not doing this for me. I'm doing it to save our kids!"

His words were met by **cheer**s and **polite applause**.

Off to the side, Arthur stood with his mother. He was holding up a sign that said, KEEP YOUR **PAW**S OFF OUR BOOKS!

Nobody seemed to be paying **attention**.

"I don't see anyone," said Arthur. "I guess WonderWorld wins."

"Don't be too sure," said Mrs. Read. "There's still time."

"This is our little girl," Ed Crosswire continued. He held up Muffy's hand. "We started PAWS because of her, but we care about all of you as well."

At that moment Buster, Francine, the Brain, and Sue Ellen came around the corner. They were holding signs over their heads.

OBEY THE **LAW**S—NOT PAWS!

CLOSE THE BOOK ON PAWS!

"You're here!" said Arthur. "I was beginning

to **wonder**."

"Sorry we're late," said the Brain. "We stopped for more **signature**s."

He **held out** the **petition sheet**s. There were now **dozen**s and dozens of names.

"So who's going to give these to Mr. Crosswire?" Buster asked.

"You do it," said the Brain.

"Not me," said Buster. "You do it."

"Who?" said Sue Ellen.

"Not you," said Francine. "How about Arthur?"

"Yeah!"

"Good idea."

"Well, Arthur . . . ," said the Brain.

Arthur took a deep **breath**. "All right," he said. "I'll do it!"

Holding the petitions under one arm, he worked his way through the crowd.

No Ferris wheel.* No sno-cones.* No roller

coaster.

"Excuse me. Excuse me. Coming through."

No cotton candy.* No bumper cars. No **haunt**ed house.*

At the top of the steps, Arthur stopped in front of Mr. Crosswire. He would be sorry to **miss** all those great things at WonderWorld. But this was more important.

"If we don't **take a stand** now, we will have **fail**ed in our trust. We must—"

"Excuse me, please, Mr. Crosswire," said Arthur. "We need to talk."

"Not now, Arthur. I'm **on a roll**."

"**That's just it**, Mr. Crosswire. You're **rol**ling right over our **right**s. It's not **fair**. Speaking for the kids, we really want our books back.

★ Ferris wheel 유원지에 있는 관람차.
✳ sno-cones 원추형의 종이컵에 깎은 얼음 조각을 넣고 시럽을 뿌린 빙수.
✳ cotton candy 솜사탕.
✳ haunted house 귀신의 집.

We've got these signatures of **support**—"

"That's nice, Arthur. I **admire** your **spirit**. But believe me, this is for your own **good**! These books are trouble with a **capital** *T*.★"

"Have you read them?" asked a voice from the crowd.

Arthur turned around. That voice was **familiar**.

Surprisingly, it was familiar to Ed Crosswire, too. He looked out over the crowd. He seemed a little **confuse**d.

Arthur wondered what would happen next.

★ **with a capital A, B, . . .** 그야말로, 정말로, 진짜로. 특정한 단어의 의미를 강조할 때, 그 단어의 첫 글자를 대문자로 써서 나타내는 표현법이다. 여러 상황에서 다양하게 확장하여 사용할 수 있다. He was romantic with a capital R. 그는 그야말로 낭만적이었다. You are wrong with a capital W. 너는 완전히 틀렸다.

Chapter
9

"Who is that?" asked Ed Crosswire.

The rest of the **crowd** was silent.

"Answer the question," said the voice. "Have you read the books you're **condemn**ing?"

The crowd **pull**ed **back** to **reveal** the speaker. Arthur **recognize**d her. She was the woman he had spoken with in the park.

Mr. Crosswire cleared his **throat**. "I am proud to say that I wouldn't read these books if you paid me!"

The woman **sigh**ed. "I'm not **surprise**d," she said.

Mr. Crosswire looked **startled**. "Why, I know you. . . . You're Miss McWord, my grade-school★ English teacher."

"Yes, I am, Edward." She walked up the steps. "I'm glad to see your **memory** hasn't **fail**ed you—even if your **common sense** has."

"Miss McWord, I **assure** you I have every **bit** as much common sense as I ever did."

She stood beside him. "That may be true," she **admit**ted. "I see you haven't changed. You never were much of a reader. Can you **appreciate** how hard a writer works to **create** stories kids will like to read? Each story is like a **seed**, Edward. If a child reads one, the seed may grow into the **desire** to read another. That's something every writer hopes for."

Mr. Crosswire **cross**ed his arms. "Oh,

★ grade-school (= elementary school) 초등학교.

really? Miss McWord, you were **certainly** a **fine** teacher. But what makes you such an **expert** about what writers hope for?"

"Well, I'm a writer myself."

"Oh. I'm sure we're all **delight**ed to hear that." Mr. Crosswire **hesitate**d. "Anything we'd know?"

Miss McWord **straighten**ed Mr. Crosswire's jacket and **flick**ed some **lint** from his shoulder. "Nothing you've read, Edward, **consider**ing your common sense and all. But since you've asked, I'm the **author** of the Scare-Your-Pants-Off Club books."

"You!" said Mr. Crosswire, turning **pale**. He had a sudden **vision** of Miss McWord walking him down to the **principal**'s office.

"You?" said Arthur.

"Her?" Francine, Buster, Sue Ellen, and the Brain said together.

The woman **nod**ded. "E. A. D'Poe is my

pen name.★"

Muffy nearly **explode**d with excitement. "Ms. D'Poe!" she cried. "I'm your number-one fan! I have all your books. Could I have your—" Her parents **glare**d at her. "Oooops!"

She **clasp**ed her hand across her mouth as her parents **surround**ed her.

"You read them all?" said her father.

"And just when did you do that?" asked her mother. "Mary Alice Crosswire, you've got some **fancy** explaining to do."

"Uh-oh!" said Muffy.

"If you've read all of these books," said Mrs. Crosswire, "then **obvious**ly it wasn't one of them that gave you the **nightmare**. What was it?"

"Um, well . . ." Muffy hated it when her mother sounded like a **detective**.

★ **pen name** 필명. 글을 써서 발표할 때 사용하는, 본명이 아닌 이름.

"Just a minute, here," said Mr. Crosswire. He **stare**d at Muffy. "Now I know who ate my quart★ of Haasen-Pfeffer ice cream."

"And then was **afraid** to admit it," said her mother. "Mary Alice, you know eating like that gives you bad dreams."

"We're very **disappoint**ed in you," said her father.

"And I'm disappointed in you, too," Muffy's mother said to her husband. "What were you doing with a quart of that ice cream, anyway?"

"Well, I . . ."

Arthur almost smiled. Muffy and her father were both standing with their heads **hang**ing low. They looked very much **alike**.

Miss McWord cleared her throat. "I hate to **interrupt** a **promising** family **squabble**,

---

★ **quart** 액량의 단위 쿼트. 1쿼트는 1/4갤런, 약 1리터이다.

but we've still got some business to **settle**. Edward, maybe you can take your foot out of your mouth* long enough to listen to one of my stories. That way you can make an **inform**ed decision about who should be reading them."

"Oh. Yes. Excellent idea."

At this **particular** moment, anything was better than **facing** his wife.

★**take your foot out of your mouth** 실언을 했다고 할 때 'put one's foot in one's mouth'라는 표현을 사용하는데, 직역하면 '입 안에 발을 집어넣다'는 의미이다. 본문에서는 이와 반대로 실언을 수습한다는 의미에서 '입에서 발을 꺼낸다'고 표현하고 있다.

Chapter 10

*"And since that night, nobody has **dared** to **steal** anything from the **haunt**ed hamburger **stand** again."*

Miss McWord put down her book.

The crowd **clap**ped and **cheer**ed. Among the loudest fans was Ed Crosswire.

"Well, Daddy?" Muffy asked.

He **sigh**ed. "I guess I shouldn't have tried to stop you kids from reading books without knowing the whole story myself."

"Maybe," said Miss McWord, "you have changed some, **after all**, Edward."

"So can we have our books back, Mr. Crosswire?" Arthur asked.

"I will **disband** PAWS on one **condition**," said Mr. Crosswire.

Everyone fell silent.

"And that condition is?" said Muffy.

"That Miss McWord will read us another story." Mr. Crosswire looked at her. "Please?"

"Yes!"

"Another one!"

"All right!"

Miss McWord smiled, something she didn't do very often. She **crack**ed open another book.

*"No one in the **village** knew why the old man lived all alone, deep in the dark woods. Only the animals of the **forest** knew his secret. . . ."*

Arthur sat back and closed his eyes as a **familiar chill crept** up his **spine**.